D1267863

The Psychology of BIRDS

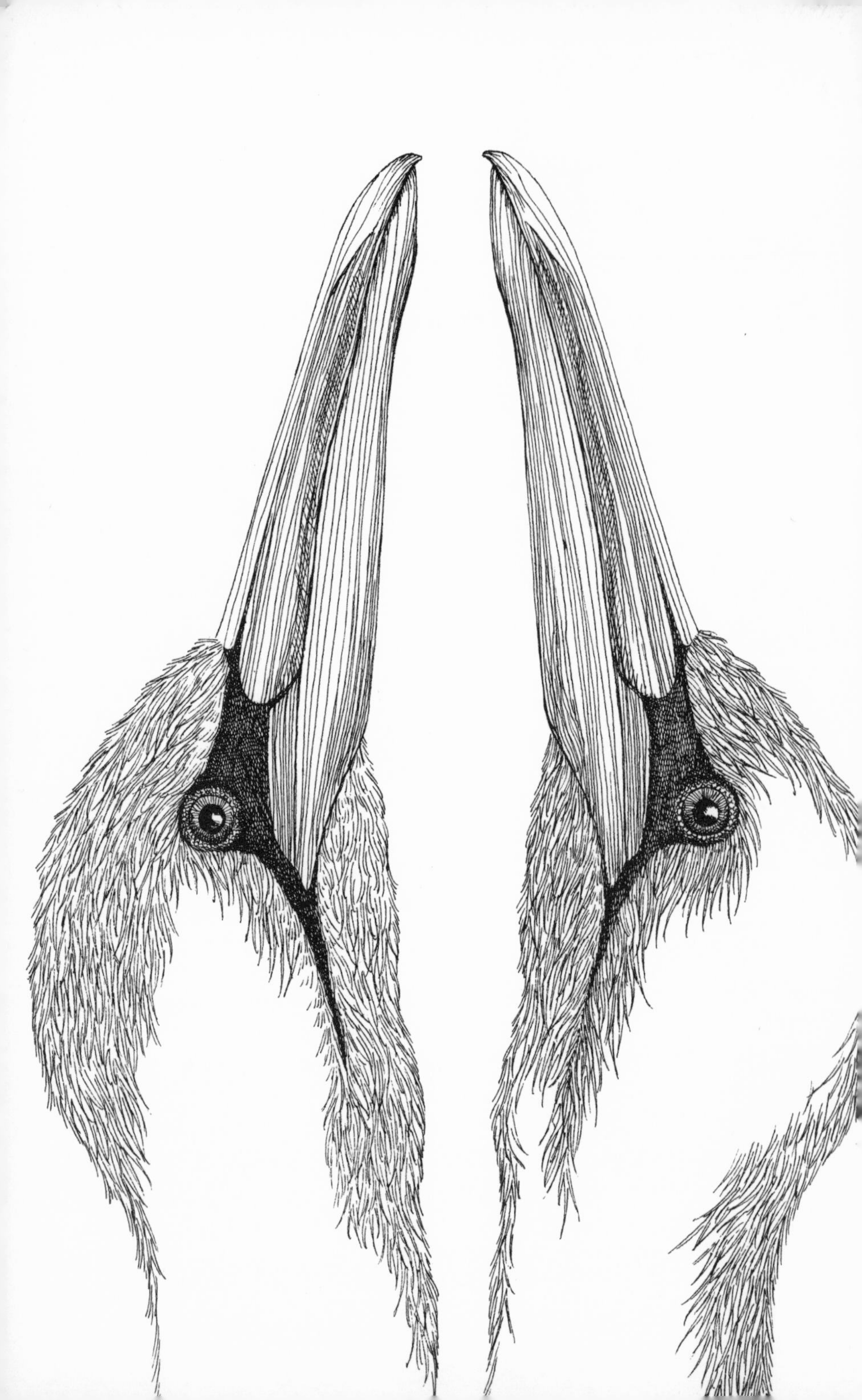

The Psychology of
BIRDS

AN INTERPRETATION OF BIRD BEHAVIOR

Harold E. Burtt, Ph.D.

Professor Emeritus of Psychology, Ohio State University

Illustrations by Peter Parnall

The Macmillan Company / New York

COLLIER-MACMILLAN LIMITED, LONDON

Library of Congress Catalog Card Number: 67-12222

FIRST PRINTING

THE MACMILLAN COMPANY, NEW YORK
COLLIER-MACMILLAN CANADA LTD., TORONTO, ONTARIO

PRINTED IN THE UNITED STATES OF AMERICA

T O *D O T*

CONTENTS

CHAPTER I

The Approach to Bird Psychology

Who's Interested in Birds?

Several kinds of people are interested in birds. Most conspicuous are the bird watchers, who roam the countryside with binoculars and small telescopes, spending their time identifying the birds they encounter and keeping annual records. With some 650 species of birds in the United States, the watchers are not likely to run out of birds, but they are especially interested in finding the bird unusually early or late or of a rare species. This all makes for a certain amount of rivalry, or camaraderie, as the case may be, among the observers, depending on the personalities involved.

The professional ornithologists constitute the second group. They represent a branch of biological science and study practically everything about birds: how they developed in the course of evolution; how the individual survives, including food, feeding habits, fighting when necessary, migrating to a suitable climate; how the species survives, including breeding, nesting, rearing young; structure and growth of the body; classification of species; distribution of species around the world; and communication by way of song or posture.

The third group is made up of psychologists. Theirs is both a biological and a social science, and they are concerned with experience and behavior. Their interest in the lower animals, including birds, is to quite an extent due to the way studies of animal psychology contribute to better understanding of human psychology. Many of the theoretical principles which govern human behavior were worked out with laboratory animals. You can do things to animals that you cannot do to humans, such as remove part of the brain. The science, of course, is much broader than this and extends into many practical fields such as education, medicine, law and business.

There is, in addition, the occasional psychologist who is also a bird watcher. As he goes afield he identifies the bird, of course, but also notes what it is doing and speculates as to why. He tries to put the observed behavior into some existing psychological framework. Maybe he starts bird banding in collaboration with the U.S. Wildlife Service. This involves trapping wild birds and putting numbered aluminum bands on their legs. Banding helps the Service unravel some problems about migration or length of life, for example. It also gives the psychologist a chance to handle the birds and observe differences in behavior at close range. If he photographs birds while he is concealed in a blind, he sees some interesting activity in more detail and occasionally gets a picture to document it. Then he begins to read journals of ornithology and finds many studies reported or in progress that have psychological implications; in these his background helps him to interpret the behavior described. Then he writes a book about bird psychology.

What Psychology Is About

Psychology deals with experience and behavior. But even at the human level, the psychologist stresses behavior more than "conscious experience." It is difficult to find the causes of behavior in the experience. A man can report how he *feels* in a certain situation, but it is his nervous system that determines what he *does*. His conscious states are private and cannot be judged objectively. Such judgments may be incorrect, as when he has hallucinations and hears voices insulting him although he is alone in a room.

Everyone is a psychologist in a small way and has picked up some common-sense notions about human behavior in the course of just living with people. Some regularities have been observed often enough to suggest a general principle. Even the small child learns to expect different results according to whether his mother scowls or smiles. The salesman knows he always can get the attention of a certain prospect by talking about fishing. Even the football cheering section yells "fight" rather than "relax." The amateur psychologist makes some mistakes, such as basing a principle on a very few instances when he really should have had a hundred, but he is at least on the fringes of science. If he shifts his concern from human psychology to bird psychology, he will be making observations and drawing conclusions in practically the same fashion and may find it equally interesting.

The psychologist finds one major difference between his approach to man and to lower animals. With the latter he cannot tap the conscious-experience aspect at all for the very good reason that animals cannot talk. It is useless to ask the blue jay why he is screaming. But, if we see a cat slinking through the shrubbery, we are pretty certain what is stimulating the jay, and it is a reasonable assumption that he is either afraid or angry. But this is only an assumption on the basis of how we would feel if we saw a predator roaming *our* neighborhood.

Be Careful in Interpretation

The psychologist is cautious in such interpretations. He can note the stimulus that strikes the bird's sense organs and he can observe the resulting response of its muscular system. Stimulus and response are sufficient for prediction of what the organism will do. This principle operates even at the human level. We give a man some psychological tests and predict how successful he will be in a particular job. But curiosity—even scientific curiosity—tempts one to look behind (or alongside) the behavior for the conscious-experience part that makes the bird more interesting as another living individual rather than just a mechanism full of nerve fibers. But we must not push this too far. Uncritical interpretations of animal behavior can get out of bounds.

In psychology we have a principle called the law of parsimony, which tempers such uncritical interpretations. It recommends that we should not explain the behavior by a higher-level process when we can interpret it adequately by a lower-level process. Suppose we see a house wren picking up a stick by one end and pulling it through the small entrance to his house rather than taking it by the middle and getting stuck with it across the hole. Ahah! The bird had insight into the geometry of the situation, figured that the length of the stick was greater than the diameter of the hole and acted accordingly. On the contrary, if we had been around earlier we would have seen him vainly holding sticks by the middle dozens of times and then eventually blundering into grasping one by the end and being rewarded by success; after many of these blunders and successes he finally learned how to do it. His "insight" actually was a rather low level of hit-and-miss learning (or trial-and-error, as we more frequently call it). That is the only safe explanation. If we do not stick to these lower-level interpretations, there is no telling where we shall end. If we attribute insight to the wren and go on from there, he may presently wind up with immortality and go to a wren heaven after the cat gets his earthly carcass.

Therefore, in our subsequent discussion if we mention the bird's sensations, feelings or emotions, it is with the reservation that we are dealing only by analogy to human experience. Bird behavior is interesting in itself, but it is even more so, on occasion, when we consider the "as if" aspect.

TWO WAYS TO APPROACH BIRD PSYCHOLOGY

WATCHING BIRDS UNDER NATURAL CONDITIONS / The methods used in the study of bird behavior and/or psychology fall into two types: natural observation and experiment. The former in its simpler aspects may involve the mere collection of anecdotes (well authenticated, hopefully) or casual observation of bird behavior while one is doing something else. For example, one glances out the window on a spring morning and sees a male cardinal in the driveway. He picks up a bit of food, moves over and feeds it to a female who is standing nearby. If this is noted on several occasions, it may occur to the observer that he has not seen such behavior at other times of the year, so it looks like "young man's fancy" in the spring. Anyone can make observations of this sort and may find it interesting to keep records. A bird diary eventually may yield some worthwhile scientific information.

Rather than waiting for things to happen incidentally, one may set out on a systematic project of observing birds in their natural surroundings. For instance, one may sit with his binoculars in a blind made of burlap at the edge of a colony where gulls are nesting, observing everything he can and taking copious notes. He tries to record every threat, every fight, every scream, all the comings and goings, how frequently the young gulls eat, who sits on the eggs and for how long, how the unattached or "eligible" members pose and posture in the process of interesting some other party. This type of observation requires a bit of know-how and certainly patience, but many amateurs as well as professionals participate.

THE EXPERIMENTAL METHOD / In this method, one makes changes in the bird's surroundings to see what will happen. This can be done to some extent in the field. Suppose we are interested in the tendency for a goose to roll a misplaced egg back into the nest. If we place near the nest objects that resemble eggs in varying degrees and note which ones are rolled by the goose, we find that an artificial egg much larger than normal or even a cylinder will suffice to touch off the rolling response.

More frequently, however, the experimental work is done in a laboratory or in an equivalent enclosed area outdoors. Here we are able to control carefully the stimuli presented to the birds and can record, sometimes automatically, the responses they make. Suppose that at the time of fall migration, when they are getting restless, some birds are placed in what is essentially a planetarium with artificial stars overhead. The margin of the cage is equipped with perches that make electric contacts when the birds are on them. Pens record on a moving paper tape how many times the birds perch on the north side and the south side of the area. What we are getting at is whether during migration birds navigate by the stars. If it is autumn and the planetarium shows the major stars about as they appear in the fall and the birds tend to perch primarily on the south side of the cage, it appears that they are influenced somewhat by the stars. There could be some other cue, but we check that by turning the planetarium to show the summer stars. If the birds then fly in all directions, that tends to confirm our hypothesis about their navigation.

WHICH IS BETTER— FIELD OR LABORATORY?

EACH of the foregoing approaches has its enthusiasts and its opponents. Some consider that the laboratory is such an artificial situation that the birds will not reveal their natural behavior. For instance, if they do not have to fight for food, they may lose some of their aggressiveness. Their "escape" tendencies are minimized because there is no place to go. A robin who has never been attacked by a sharp-shinned hawk may be different from robins who have had that experience.

On the other hand, in the wild you cannot control all the factors in the situation to find what actually influences the bird. One essential of scientific method is to change one variable at a time and see what happens. Suppose you want to know just what aspect of the parent's bill, when it appears near the nest, leads the young gull to peck at that bill for food. Is it the shape, color or position? Watching gulls under natural conditions, you could never tell. But it is possible experimentally to present a young gull with targets made of cardboard painted different colors, of varying shapes and at varying angles. These aspects can be changed one at a time while counting how frequently the young bird pecks at the target. It may develop that almost any kind of object with a reddish blotch on the lower end does the trick.

In our subsequent discussion we shall draw on field or laboratory data without prejudice, providing that they contribute something of interest. Of course we shall be on the alert for possible factors that might upset the field observations and for "unnatural" elements in the laboratory situation.

Preview of the Book

The sense organs / At this point let's take a look at the topics to be discussed in succeeding chapters. We shall begin with the bird's contact with the external world—what he gets through his sense organs. Vision is rather important to a bird hovering 100 feet in the air and watching for a field mouse. Actually, birds have about the keenest vision of any animal. A thrush can see a hawk so high in the air that a man must use binoculars to see it. Birds can see colors, which presumably makes plumage more important. They are quite good at telling the distance of an object; otherwise they would miss a meal at which they were diving or they might let a dangerous enemy get too close.

Birds depend a great deal on their ears. Try to sneak up on them unnoticed or even to open a window surreptitiously. They may not be able to hear all the notes of the piano as we do, but at least they can hear the sounds made by their own species. Some birdsongs are so high in the scale that many people cannot hear them. Try listening to a bay-breasted warbler or a grasshopper sparrow, for example.

Many birds are quite adept at locating the direction of a sound. A barn owl can dive directly at a scurrying mouse in total darkness with only sound to guide him. At least one bird uses a kind of sonar technique, sending out a series of squeaks that are reflected back from objects. Bats do this most effectively. We know little about taste and smell in birds.

Then there is the question of just what part of the situation actually stimulates the bird. We have mentioned that it is the red spot on the parent gull's bill that triggers the young one's food reaction. A cardboard target with a short head and long tail placed above the pen will frighten ducks if it moves "head first" but is ignored when moving in the other direction. The former situation resembles a hawk and the latter a goose. In other cases any "swooping" object—even a model airplane—will alert some birds.

It is important for birds to distinguish friend from foe. But they do make mistakes, just as we sometimes slap the wrong person on the back. They will attack a small stuffed owl when a good part of it is missing, or they will fight their own reflection in a window or an automobile hubcap. Then there is the question of whether or not they recognize members of their own family, especially the young. With reference to the latter there is some evidence in both directions. Where a colony of penguins have a communal nursery, the parents feed inmates rather indiscriminately as though they did not recognize their own. On the other hand, if a small gull gets loose from an island and takes off by himself down the lake, it is only the two parents who give chase and convoy him back to safety. Obviously they have recognized Junior.

DRIVES AND MOTIVES / The next question is what the bird does in response to these stimuli from the external world. He doesn't do anything unless he has some drive or motive. Otherwise the stimulus just "goes in one ear and out the other." A drive makes the bird active, and when the object of the drive has been achieved, the strength of the drive is reduced or disappears altogether. To a hungry bird flying overhead, the sight of corn on a feeder will lead him to drop down. After he has eaten, the drive departs and so does the bird; he does something else until he gets hungry again.

Hunger is one of the most important drives in the bird's equipment, which is one reason that food is used in trapping birds or in getting them to come to a particular spot where they can be watched or photographed. But even a basic drive like this is influenced by the situation involved. When hungry birds have to perform an experimental task such as running through a maze in order to get food, they run faster when there is a large amount of food at the end than when there is a small amount. In a situation where a bird is allowed to eat as much as it wishes, it often will eat more when other eaters are present than when it is alone. We do this ourselves. A man who eats sparingly at home gorges himself at a potluck dinner. The need for water is another drive closely related to that for food.

Escaping from danger is a common drive. The bird recognizes the danger in some fashion, whereupon the drive operates. But the exact pattern varies with the species. A frightened song sparrow dives into the nearest shrubbery. A vesper sparrow, on the other hand, goes practically "up out of sight."

Another drive comes from the sex glands. The changes in the daylight/darkness ratio and in temperature are not sufficient to start the northward migration in the spring without some help from the glands.

Something akin to curiosity leads birds to come toward a sound of alarm or distress notes. If a robin is in trouble and is vociferous, a dozen other robins appear. A standard procedure for getting birds out into view is to arouse their curiosity by making a "pish" sound or a squeak that suggests distress.

Some drives are periodic or seasonal. We have mentioned annual migration and at the end of the trip, of course, there is mating. The periodic urge to build a nest has led some birds in search of building material to perch on a man's head and try to pull out some hair. The drive is strong enough to offset the fear tendency that prevails the rest of the year.

Instinct / Turning now to the behaviors that result from contact with the outer world, facilitated by the drives, we find two kinds: instinctive behavior and learned behavior. The former is unlearned and hereditary. While there is considerable controversy at the human level about the comparative importance of these two, there is no question with birds—instinct plays a very large role with them and it is surprisingly effective. Instinctive tendencies have evolved in the species by survival of the fittest. A bird that inherited the tendency to build an insecure nest would not have any offspring to carry on that insecurity; offspring of good nest builders would survive and pass this characteristic along to the next generation.

We shall note a couple of ways in which instincts are useful to birds. The first is that they contribute to individual survival. Take, for instance, certain innate tendencies in connection with food getting. The turnstone (one of the shorebirds) does just what his name implies: he turns over small stones on the beach with his bill. He then eats insects that cling to the underside of the stone or hide beneath. The utility of this behavior is obvious and all turnstones practice it.

Again, the tendency to flee from danger does not involve indiscriminate running in any direction. Birds that are vulnerable to attack by predators from overhead instinctively move to get under something or into thick brush. Those whose natural enemies are animals on the ground do their escaping in an upward direction.

The other utility of instincts contributes to continuance of the species. Mating is basic, of course, but nest construction is also important if the eggs are to survive. Even a bird that has never seen a nest constructed proceeds to make one in the same pattern as do all members of its species—sometimes a very complicated pattern. Incubating the eggs and then feeding the nestlings are irresistible tendencies. The urge to put something in an open mouth is so strong that the food often gets in the wrong mouth; a bird carrying nesting material may, on occasion, pass a loud, open mouth in a nearby nest and cram it full of dried grass.

But instinctive behavior is rather inflexible and if something goes wrong in a situation, the bird will react in the same old way. Gulls drop shellfish on the rocks to crack them open. Sometimes, however, when rocks are not handy, they drop this potential food on soft mud. A species of woodpecker that stores acorns in small holes in trees will, on occasion, put them in a hole that goes through the tree so that they drop out on the far side. There is a surprising lack of resourcefulness in all this.

A bird does not exhibit his whole instinctive repertoire as soon as he is hatched. His muscular equipment is not equal to it. But the tendency is there in his genes and comes out at the right time.

When a young duck gets out of the nest and starts to walk, it is ready to follow its mother around. Actually, the instinctive tendency that appears on schedule is to follow a moving object. Usually the moving object present at the crucial moment is the mother, and the instinct of following quickly specializes on the mother duck, but there are cases where a man happened to move by at just the right (or wrong) time, whereupon the duckling followed him and then tended to follow people for the rest of its life.

Migration / This dramatic case of instinctive behavior is worthy of discussion in its own right. It may involve great distances, such as the tern going from the Arctic to the Antarctic. There are fairly well-defined flyways along which birds go south for the winter, and when they come back in the spring, they may return to the same region they left, sometimes even to the same nest.

One question is what starts them off at the right time. We are not entirely sure, although we know some of the stimuli. Changes in temperature and daylight are involved in the general schedule. Winds, storms and weather fronts may produce delays or accelerations. The operation of the sex glands in the spring has been mentioned above and is an indispensable stimulus.

The other major question about migration is how birds navigate. Some, hatched in the north, take off by themselves with no parents along and follow the ancestral route south. Some species can hit a small island in mid-ocean. To some extent there may be landmarks like rivers or coastlines and birds also use the sun, but a great deal of migration takes place at night. The possibility of using the stars was mentioned earlier. The human navigator, however, needs printed tables and accurate clocks. Much research is being conducted on the particular question of bird navigation—especially celestial navigation.

Learned behavior / Our next consideration is learned behavior. While birds inherit a large portion of their behavior tendencies, on occasion they do learn. The act of flying, for instance, gets smoothed out by practice, as when flying in a strong wind. Two types of learning may be mentioned that involve somewhat different principles. Trial-and-error learning was mentioned earlier and illustrated by the wren's learning to pick up sticks by the end. It was characterized by many futile attempts to solve the problem, accidental success that was rewarded or "reinforced" and eventually enough successful experiences to establish the habit.

It is important, however, for the reinforcement to occur at the right time so as to be associated with the right act. A bird goes into a maze-type trap used for some scientific purpose and gets food (reward) and presently finds that he cannot get out (punishment). Subsequently he may enter the trap again and again because the punishment did not occur at the time he entered. It is a bit like the child whose discipline is postponed until Father gets home at night. He has difficulty connecting the belated punishment with the crime.

The other type of learning is illustrated by a blackbird that followed a boat on the Great Lakes. It perched near the pilothouse, where the pilot was swatting flies. He threw some of the dead flies to the bird. After a number of experiences of this sort, the bird learned to come to the pilothouse when it heard the swatter in operation. The response of coming at the sight of dead flies was transferred to coming at the sound of the swatter. Technically, we say the response was "conditioned," and a great deal of learning follows this pattern.

An instance of learning that is perhaps more appropriate in the discussion of social behavior is learning who is boss of the flock. Instead of fighting at every feeding time, they settle it once and for all by establishing a "peck order" and thereafter take turns in that order. Then, too, there is the learning situation where a wild bird becomes tame. Young crows have often been converted into pets. A friend of the writer's had a young grackle that had fallen from the nest and was reared in captivity until capable of going out on its own. After it had been turned loose, one could step out on the porch and say, "Hi, Pete," and there would be an answering squawk from the shrubbery and Pete would fly over to take a tidbit from one's hand. This behavior lasted for several weeks until the urge to flock with the other grackles prevailed.

In the laboratory there have been many experiments in teaching birds a variety of responses, some of which will be discussed in due course. It is even possible to teach them a completely useless habit. Pigeons were taught, when approaching the food box, to stop and make a complete clockwise turn before eating. Moreover, learning techniques have been used in the laboratory in the investigation of sensory discrimination. We may teach a bird to go to a food hopper every time a note is sounded. Then we raise the pitch of the note higher and higher till the bird no longer goes to the hopper. Thus we determine the limit of the bird's hearing range.

Social behavior / The external world from which the bird gets its stimulation includes not only physical things like trees and food but also other birds. These are social stimuli. Humans are outstandingly social animals; birds are less so, but show enough social behavior to warrant its discussion.

One aspect is the tendency to get together in flocks. Anyone who has seen a quarter million blackbirds (actually a combination of smaller flocks of grackles, cowbirds, starlings and red-wings) pouring into a roost at sunset cannot but be impressed by this social manifestation that often precedes migration. A hundred avocets will gather in a compact mass on a small muddy spot and mill around in unison in a circular pattern. The function of this gathering is problematical.

On occasion, the gathering of birds involves something akin to cooperation. Robins will "gang up" on a cat, make a lot of noise and even dive at it. If you hear a number of crows calling and see a concentration in the vicinity of a particular tree, look for a hawk or an owl there. They seldom do him any harm but cooperate in trying to make him miserable.

When many birds get together, there is a good opportunity for fights to develop. Some of these serve to establish the peck order just mentioned. Many such encounters occur at the breeding season, when a male defends his nest territory against other males who intrude.

Social activities are not confined to members of one species; in winter one may note chickadees, titmice and nuthatches moving around together. Some species associate with large mammals in the interest of simplifying the food problem. Magpies for instance, feed on insects that in turn are feeding on the back of a deer. This helps both magpies and deer.

Antisocial behavior appears among birds, as it does in man.

Theft is not uncommon. English sparrows will take a worm from a robin that has just pulled it from the burrow. One robin has been seen to lose six worms in immediate succession in this way. More dramatic is the eagle, which "holds up" the osprey in mid-air to make it drop a fish, which the eagle then retrieves.

There are also the social parasites. The female cowbird lays an egg or two in the nest of, say, a chipping sparrow, which then hatches and feeds the young cowbirds. Sometimes the young "chippies" hold their own, but all too often the young cowbirds, being larger, get all the food brought to the nest.

COMMUNICATION / Social behavior is facilitated by some form of communication, some of which is nonvocal and by posture or gesture. In many species, a lowered head thrust forward with wings slightly spread and feathers fluffed says "move on" or at least denotes a threat. When a bird goes courting, it may point its bill straight up or bob its head up and down in eloquent fashion. More usually observed, however, are the various songs and call notes. These differ greatly from species to species. Song is one of the cues that bird watchers use in identifying species in the field, especially after the leaves have come out and obscured visual identification. With the development of portable tape recorders, more thorough study of birdsongs has been made possible. They can be investigated in detail by appropriate electrical analyzers. Long-playing records are available to help one learn to recognize the different songs.

The songs and calls may be classified according to their functions. A common type is the "advertising" song. This may announce that the male is "on territory." Many of the beautiful songs that to us suggest romance are essentially "get out of here" warnings or even worse. To be sure, the advertisement may also suggest to any females within range that the locale of the advertisement would be a good place in which to nest. Perhaps this is stretching the interpretation a bit, but at least the males keep away and a female comes along.

Other notes indicate some need, such as the food call of young birds, who even if they fall out of the nest continue to yell for food till the parents find them. (Incidentally it is better, if one finds young out of the nest, to replace them in the nest or to put them up on a bush or some place where they are safe from predators and to let the adults resume operations at the new stand. Otherwise, the Good Samaritan lets himself in for an exacting several-times-an-hour feeding schedule for a few weeks.)

Bird language is limited to what in English usage would be exclamations. One note merely indicates distress or danger. Crows have a sort of assembly call that they give when they sight an enemy. It is interesting to record songs or calls on tape and play them back to the birds. On occasion they will gather around and even attack the loudspeaker. When distress calls are played, the birds may scatter.

Careful analysis of the tapes makes it possible to sort out the inherited and the acquired parts. Apparently a certain pattern, such as a sustained trill, is innate for a given species but then modifications are made as the youngster hears other birds. He adopts a "standard" duration and adds a characteristic terminal flourish.

Family problems / One other segment of social behavior is that which takes place in the small bird group analogous to the human family. Establishing territory by the male has been mentioned already. This includes songs and sometimes fights. Then as the females come along there may be some courtship activity. With some ducks this takes the form of posturing by moving the head up and down. The flicker's prenuptial ritual includes drumming on a dead tree. The woodcock flies up from his territory about seventy feet in the air and then dives at high speed, making bubbly notes meanwhile.

An interesting consideration about mating is its permanence. There are indications that chickadees, eagles and hawks, for instance, pair for life. Migrants such as robins often remain together throughout the trip and southern sojourn, but they sometimes get separated and then find each other next spring, when both parties return to the same area. On the other hand, some species are polygamous. They pick up a new mate every year. The male house wren does even better, often maintaining two families simultaneously in two boxes in the same back yard. Song sparrows have been known to steal each other's mates. These experiences do not appear to be as traumatic to the birds as they would be to us, and they are, of course, devoid of moral implications.

Next comes the business of building a nest. The killdeer merely uses a small hollow scooped among some small stones on the ground, while an oriole weaves a complicated engineering creation that hangs from the end of a branch. The partners may collaborate in building or one may do most of it. The male house wren hopefully fills the house with sticks all by himself. Then the female comes along and throws them all out and begins again.

The eggs must be kept reasonably warm until they hatch. Here, again, the parents in some species take turns, but if the female does most of it the male may bring food to her. When the young have to be fed, it generally requires both parents, for it is an exacting job. A nest of young phoebes was observed for an entire day and were fed 845 times in that period. A pair of chickadee parents made 35 food runs to the nest in 30 minutes. Metabolism at a tender age is rapid, obviously.

One other activity is necessary before the family cycle is complete, and that is to keep away predators, which include cats, snakes and larger birds; even a well-intentioned man may be considered a threat by a parent bird. If he climbs to a hawk's nest to band the nestlings, he may be buzzed. A killdeer tries to lure away a person too near the nest by putting on a broken-wing act.

PERSONALITY AND INTELLIGENCE / There has been little systematic investigation of the personality and intelligence of birds. These characteristics highlight differences between individuals at the human level and help us to predict what an individual will do —what can be expected of a particular pupil in school on the basis of his intelligence test, or whether an emotionally disturbed person can be trusted to drive an automobile.

There are some indications of personality differences in birds. Take aggressiveness as an example. Anyone who has had occasion to handle wild birds has been bitten by some cardinals but not by others. The peck order described elsewhere reflects differences in aggressiveness. That is how No. 1 established himself. The order might have been achieved merely by threatening postures or have required actual fighting. Aggressive birds fight not only their own species but also other species, even a stuffed model, and they have been known to attack some mammals, including humans. This is more likely to occur in the nesting season. Modification of aggressive personality is possible when a wild bird becomes tame.

Then there are "deviations" in personality. Some young birds recently out of the nest continue to beg for food from the parents while others show more maturity and strike out on their own. Polygamy, though considered a deviation by our standards, is commonplace in birds. An occasional bird may appear abnormally emotional; for instance, there was one case recorded of death from fright.

There are no tests of intelligence for birds. Occasionally we may note some differences in adaptability to a new situation, which comes pretty close. In learning situations there are some differences in rate of progress, which may reflect basic aptitudes. We are more likely to notice intelligence differences between species than between individuals. Some types of geese, for instance, will starve when their natural food is not available, but crows will rustle a substitute food in the emergency. A few ornithologists have expressed opinions as to the comparative intelligence of some species on the basis of general observations. But on the whole, personality and intelligence constitute largely a wide-open field in bird psychology.

Bird Psychology and You

The foregoing is roughly the ground we propose to cover in our discussion. It is hoped that for some readers the book will do more than just provide information and that it may have some impact on their spare-time activities. Being a psychologist, the writer has been alert to the interests and enthusiasms of bird people as well as to the birds themselves. He has seen adults develop this interest from scratch and get a whole new outlook on life. He has seen youngsters start with a few well-guided childhood experiences and go on to professional careers in ornithology. He is aware of the way that hobbies contribute to better life adjustment. This is especially important today in view of increasing leisure and resultant monotony. Outdoor hobbies have the further advantage of improved health, so it may be worth while to trace some of the steps through which a typical person might go in the development of this avocation.

Suppose that at the outset our typical person merely maintains a bird bath or feeder in the yard. This equipment presently becomes more than an ornament. He may become interested in what goes on around the feeder—whether the starlings fight over the cracked corn or take their turns; whether robins' bathing is an individual or a communal affair. Then he watches a bit more systematically, to see what happens morning, noon and night. He finds birds singing at daylight, building nests in the morning when straws and dried grasses are moist and pliant, bathing and preening in the sun at midday and having a big evening meal.

Alertness to bird behavior carries over into situations away from home. If a bird flies across the field of view anywhere the person takes another look. If a bird sings, one is inclined to stop and listen, try to figure out who is doing it and see him if possible. The song of a bird in the woods is attractive in itself but many find it a richer experience to know it is a wood thrush or, better still, if we can see the singer.

By this time our friend is ready for a pocket field guide to birds to aid in identification and binoculars for close observation. As soon as he can identify all the birds in the neighborhood he starts afield—over by the river, along the edge of the woods, in the swamp or along the hedgerow, according to what he is after. He probably joins an organization of persons with similar interests, keeps a list of species seen during a given year and begins a "life list" of all the species he has ever seen. He learns to take wet feet and briar scratches in stride. As he gets more involved, he goes beyond mere bird identification, observes more systematically and keeps records of interesting behavior he has noted. He may even experiment in a small way—try different foods or a new location of the feeder, put out several varieties of nesting material and note which bird uses what. If he is also a photography hobbyist, he gets a telephoto lens and tries to photograph a nest where there is some activity. He soon learns that he must conceal himself and eventually finds himself perspiring in some sort of blind constructed for the purpose.

Some amateur organizations of bird observers approach the fringes of professional activity. They may conduct a systematic census of birds in a particular defined area at a certain time (such as Christmas week) year after year, or they may go repeatedly to an area at daybreak in the spring and plot on a map the location of the singing males. This yields, essentially, the distribution of nests by species in that area. These and other kinds of data may contribute scientific information about population trends and factors that influence them.

One more effect that this book may have on some readers is to convince them that birds are important in the scheme of things and are worth keeping around. But this necessitates adequate facilities in the way of food, shelter and nesting areas. This, in turn, has implications for the preservation of our natural resources and of areas untouched by bulldozers.

The preceding is about as far as the average amateur ornithologist goes. Some readers, of course, will already be well along in the developmental sequence just outlined, but perhaps even for them some of the discussion will have opened up some new areas of interest. The ensuing chapters will point the way to more detailed observation and interpretation of bird behavior and a more thoroughgoing and satisfying hobby. In general the writer hopes that some of his own enthusiasm for bird psychology will rub off on the readers so that a lot more people will have a lot more fun with birds.

CHAPTER II

Sensations and Perceptions of Birds

ample, the sparrow hawk hovering in the air sees his lunch crawling out from its burrow in the field below. As to safety, the bird's world is full of predators, often approaching at high speed, which must be seen in time to permit escape. The bird, however, does not always discriminate between real and actual danger. He just "escapes," regardless. The ducks fly up from the river when an observer gets out of his car for a better look; the movement of a window shade scatters the occupants of the feeder. Evidently the birds' primary tendency is to play it safe and flee at the sight of any sudden moving large object. Much of the time such an object *is* dangerous. If the bird stops to take a second look, the way we do, and then tries to get away if necessary, it may be too late. In any case, the point in the present context is that vision is very important for the bird.

Acuity / The bird's visual equipment and facility appear to measure up to his need. A case was noted earlier of a thrush which looked upward and registered alarm, while a man had to use binoculars in order to find the alarming hawk [31, p. 15].* The same observer reported that a hobby (small European hawk) could see a dragonfly at 200 yards whereas the man's limit was 90 yards.

In the laboratory a bird's visual acuity can be measured with appropriate instruments far too complicated to describe here, but the results bear out more casual observations. At any rate the bird usually does very well in situations where good visual acuity is needed. Like so many other characteristics, this one was presumably developed through the process of evolution. Individual birds lacking it failed to see the food or the predator and therefore did not survive. Those with this facility passed it along to their descendants.

Color vision / This ability is helpful in discriminating or recognizing objects. While many kinds of animals—dogs and cats, for example—lack it, birds have good color vision, and those that operate in the daytime are similar to man in being most sensitive to the yellow-green range of the spectrum. Experiments with a few

* Numbers in brackets indicate references by chapters at the end of the book.

species of birds have determined this sensitivity. The technique was based upon the fact that the diameter of the pupil of the eye becomes greater as light becomes dimmer. Several birds that operate in the daytime such as domestic chicken, herring gull and sparrow hawk showed the greatest sensitivity to the yellow part of the spectrum, while a nocturnal bird such as a certain species of owl showed high sensitivity to green and blue. There are two kinds of organs in the retina at the back of the eye: cones, which function primarily in daylight and are most sensitive to the yellow or yellow-green region, and rods, which function in dim light and are sensitive to green-blue. Nocturnal animals like owls have a preponderance of rods in the eye, which is why they operate so successfully at night [6].

Color vision helps birds to recognize each other. In many species the male is colored differently from the female—cardinals for example—which helps match them up quickly and correctly in the springtime. When the two sexes do not so differ in color or other markings there may be difficulty, as with song sparrows. The male sparrow may have to resort to attacking an intruder in his territory. Should it fly away, the stranger is a male, but if it squats down, it is a female [32, p. 333].

Color vision is also helpful in connection with food, helping the hummingbird to find the most favorable flowers on which to feed, for example. Also, it has been found that a red feeder attracts hummingbirds better than other colors. Another indication of color vision is the fact that a certain species of bower bird always collects blue objects to decorate the bower. Obviously the bird must discriminate colors in order to make such a selection.

BRIGHTNESS VISION / Aside from color, birds are sensitive to light and dark, an obvious manifestation being their flying to a roost in the late afternoon, when the light decreases. It might seem that other factors than darkness might vary with the time of day and start the parade toward the roost. However, we have a few authenticated instances where an eclipse of the sun occurred in the middle of the day, and birds reacted as if it were twilight. These cases were reported in scientific journals by careful observers. During an 89 per cent eclipse, a flock of sparrows flew to their ordinary night roost, and species that normally retire when the sun begins to set were more influenced by the eclipse than were species that normally retire later in the evening when it is much darker [17]. During a total eclipse, gulls left their feeding grounds and headed toward their roosting areas. Birdsong "fell off noticeably" [15], while at another location it was reported that blackbirds were silent for ten minutes and canaries for four minutes during the eclipse, although a robin sang right through it.

Visual equipment / It may be of interest to consider the visual equipment of birds as related to behavior. The eyes themselves are often quite large in proportion to the rest of the body. The great horned owl's eyes are about the same size as ours although the bird itself weighs only three or four pounds and stands about two feet tall. The larger eye admits more of the dim light in which the owl frequently operates.

The eyes of most birds except for gulls, cormorants and a few others do not turn very rapidly. Instead, the bird turns its entire head, its neck being much more flexible than ours. Owls are notorious in this respect. Have you ever tried to walk around one of them that was perched fairly low, so that you were mutually visible? He does not change his position on the perch but turns his head to watch. Unless you are extremely alert, you may conclude that his head turns 360 degrees or even more. Actually, when he is something over halfway around, he reaches his limit and the head snaps back to the initial position, but he now sees you coming instead of going. The snap is so rapid that you are likely to miss it and thus assume that the owl's head turns indefinitely.

Location of eyes / The position of the eye naturally determines what the bird can see. Those that hunt live food (predators) need to look forward, while those that are hunted need to see things on both sides and sometimes toward the rear as well, as is the case with the woodcock. He spends a lot of time probing deeply in mud with his long bill for worms. In that position he is vulnerable to attack from the rear. Accordingly his eyes are set toward the rear of the head, and the field covered jointly by the two eyes is probably much wider toward the rear than toward the front. Like us, birds use the two eyes in combination to see distance or depth—called the binocular field [33]. Hawks and owls, unlike the woodcock, have their eyes arranged to look forward. The binocular field for owls in a forward direction may be as much as 60 to 70 degrees wide and for hawks up to 50 degrees, whereas for seed-eating birds it is less than 25 degrees. The seed is stationary and thus is easier to keep in view. Then there is the bittern, which stands in the swamp among the reeds and freezes, his bill pointing straight up so that it resembles another reed. This would ordinarily point his eyes toward the sky, which, to the bittern, is unimportant. He needs to see what is going on in the swamp. So his eyes are able to turn downward to a considerable degree even though his head is pointing upward.

Some species such as robins have eyes set to the side of the head. While this tends to reduce the binocular field to the front, with a resulting limitation of depth perception, the wide field of the single eye on each side may be more important to that bird. It is possible to turn the head when an object at the side attracts attention if there is time. There is also a somewhat limited depth perception with a single eye. Another factor that helps some birds in this respect is that two objects, one above the other at approximately eye level, change the apparent distance between them as the head is moved. This may be why some shorebirds such as spotted sandpipers characteristically bob their heads up and down. They may see the shifting of an object in relation to the horizon and thus get some clue as to its distance. Similarly, when coots are swimming, the peculiar backward-and-forward motion of the head may serve this same function [35, p. 87].

Focus / There is the matter of getting the object properly focused. This is handled by the lens of the eye, which changes its curvature as the distance of the object changes (accommodation). In a fast-flying bird this must take place very rapidly and especially so as, let us say, an osprey dives. Birds had "zoom lenses" long before they were available to photographers. With the usual eye lens, things tend to blur under water. Notice the difference when you wear goggles in a swimming pool and the eyeball is not in actual contact with the water. Diving ducks have a supplementary eyelid which closes for underwater operation and possesses a small window which acts much like a contact lens, being of the right optical characteristics to bring things into focus. Some birds such as cormorants have special muscles that squeeze the lens into proper shape for submarine use. The kingfisher has two sensitive spots on his retina though at different distances from the lens. One spot is in focus when he is in the air, the other is in focus in the water. Evidently there is considerable variation in the ways evolution has taken care of these focusing problems.

One other instance of an air-to-water arrangement may be mentioned. A young green heron was found out of the nest and kept for a few days in the home of an ornithologist. At mealtime bits of food were placed on the ground in front of the bird, and he pecked at them, although in his initial efforts he consistently pecked short of the food. Herons generally feed by wading in shallow water, picking up small fish that swim below the surface. Light rays passing from water to air are bent slightly so that an object underwater actually appears farther away than it really is because of the refraction. Hence, to touch it, one must make a "correction," not reaching quite so far as is apparently necessary. This is what herons do when catching fish. The interesting point here is that the young heron in question, not in the water, made the correction nevertheless, in this case an erroneous correction. It would seem that he had an innate tendency to peck nearer than the apparent position of the object, a tendency that would be helpful when trying to catch a fish in the water. Perhaps we should not stress this single case until others have been observed or appropriate experiments made, but our conclusion seems plausible.

Hearing

Function / The other major group of stimuli that the bird receives from the world around him comes through his ears. We have mentioned already the function of hearing in perceiving potential danger. Clap your hands and the starlings will rise from the ground where they are feeding or the marsh birds will pop into view. When the sounds are made by another bird, the situation becomes more complicated, as we detail in the chapter on communication.

Birds have special distress calls to which other birds respond appropriately. Bird watchers make a squeaking sound by "kissing" the back of the hand that so resembles a distress call, if done properly, that birds react as if it were a distress call. A patch of shrubbery that originally appeared empty is suddenly populated by a dozen birds of several species looking for the bird in distress.

The food calls of nestlings stimulate the parents to do the appropriate thing, sometimes stimulating the wrong adults. On occasion, a bird, en route to its own nest with food in its beak, will be diverted by other youngsters crying for food and give it to them instead of to its own family. Young birds, straying prematurely from the nest, are usually found by the parents when they get hungry and begin to make the appropriate sounds. One can observe this by simple experiments. For instance, some young flickers while the parents were away from the nest were moved to another nesting box a short distance away. The female parent returned to the original nest with food; finding no young, she ate the food herself. Her lack of concern was somewhat disappointing to the observer. Presently, however, the young nearby began calling and she resumed feeding them as soon as they were located. In a different experiment turkeys were deafened surgically. They incubated their eggs satisfactorily but presently killed their own young, presumably because they could not hear them peep and thus regarded them as enemies or at least as strangers [29].

ACUITY / A few instances may be noted where birds show excellent ability to detect faint sounds. A woodpecker taps on a dead tree to disturb insects so that he can detect and locate them by the sounds of their moving about. A colony of carpenter ants entered a dead tree through a knothole where later a pileated woodpecker, by tapping and listening, located the ants five feet below the knothole and drilled directly into the colony [7].

Owls may utilize sounds in catching mice, as noted earlier. A barn owl was placed in absolute darkness in a room with dried leaves on the floor. When a mouse was released, the owl waited until the mouse stopped and then hit it accurately on the first pass. The owl did the same thing with a wad of paper on a string, showing that it was not reacting to heat (infrared) or an odor from the mouse [22].

Part of the story may be the fact that the barn owl, like many other large birds, has ears placed quite a distance apart. A sound on one side strikes one ear more intensely and a bit earlier than the other ear, aiding him in locating sounds. With the ears farther apart, these differences are increased and ability to locate the sound is improved. The owl just described does not lunge at any or all sounds but is apparently particularly sensitive to sounds of a rustling quality and is able to differentiate them from other sounds.

Another example of this qualitative discrimination was shown in some experiments on green-woodpecker nestlings in a hole in a tree. When the bark near the hole was scratched with the claws of a stuffed green woodpecker, the young birds would look out of the entrance much as they did when the parent arrived, but if the scratching were done with any other instrument, the nestlings acted as if frightened [4].

Sonar technique / There are at least two species of birds that use a sonar technique for locating objects and navigating in complete darkness. Bats, of course, are well known for this, but they are mammals, not birds. The oilbird of Trinidad nests in a pitch-dark cave and finds its way by "echo location," a reflection of its own sounds. These are brief clicks given at a frequency of about 7000 cycles per second, which is a rather high pitch. The birds come out at night to feed on tree fruits, but when inside the cave they must use their sonar equipment [10]. Another species, the cave swiftlet, does much the same thing [20].

Hearing range / Another aspect of the bird's hearing that has been studied to some extent is the lowest and highest tones (pitch) that are audible. Practically no species is sensitive to all notes of the piano, as we are. They do not need to be. Why should a warbler need to hear the low blast of an ocean liner? Or an owl the supersonic dog whistle? The important thing is to hear other birds, especially those of one's own species, and also sounds that may indicate food or danger.

The hearing range of some species has been measured using captive birds in the laboratory. Some of the experimenters have used a "conditioning" technique. Inasmuch as this method is also quite widely used in animal-psychology experiments, it may be described at this point. The perch or food tray where the bird spends a lot of time is wired so that an electric shock may be given by the experimenter. At this stimulus the bird naturally jumps from the perch or tray. But along with the shock we present a sound of specific pitch. If we do this repeatedly, the sound presently becomes associated with the jumping-off response. We can then omit the shock altogether, and the sound will cause the bird to jump from the perch or tray.

Technically this is called a conditioned response; that is, the bird has been conditioned to respond to the sound. The original response to the shock was an unconditioned response. Once the bird has been conditioned to jump when it hears a sound we are in a position to investigate its hearing range. If the pitch of the tone is made higher and higher the bird continues to jump for a time but presently the point is reached where the tone produces no jump. The reason is that the bird cannot hear that tone. If we lower the tone a bit, the bird jumps again, and thus we determine the upper limit of pitch that the bird can hear and, in identical fashion, the lower limit. We may then strike an average for the species.

Quite a number of species have been measured in this way although only a few will be cited here. As a general basis for comparison we may note that piano notes range from 26 to 4,096 cycles per second and that middle C is 256. Human ears are sensitive to tones from approximately 20 to 15,000 cycles, although beyond middle age they may lose much of their sensitivity to the higher tones. Some well-known ornithologists have reported trouble in hearing the warblers' songs. But there are bird species that can hear far beyond human upper limits, the chaffinch (a small, European sparrow-like bird) having a range from 200 to 29,000 cycles. We do better, however, than many birds at the lower end of the scale. The starling ranges down to only 700 cycles, mallard ducks, 300 and pheasants, 250, and these species cannot go quite as high as humans can. The great horned owl, however, can hear sounds as low as 60 cycles, which is the lowest of any bird species measured.

Ranges like the foregoing correspond somewhat to the needs of the bird to hear certain things such as other members of its own species. The great horned owl has a comparatively low "voice" and hoots at 150 cycles. This corresponds to its ability to hear low tones. The starling, on the other hand, puts out notes at about

3,475 cycles, and this comes within its hearing range. It is also important for the bird to be able to hear sounds made by other species that may be potential sources of danger, such as predators. We do not have laboratory experiments to cover this point, but when people convincingly imitate a large owl the sound disturbs species of birds that are large enough to be endangered by such an owl. Small species do not react to this sound. It is probable that they do not hear it because they need not hear it [18]. Thus, the bird's range of hearing is adequate for the situations that it is likely to encounter.

TASTE AND SMELL

THE bird's sources of information about the world are not confined to its eyes and ears. We know less, however, about the other senses. In the field of taste, for example, very little experimental work has been done. Most writers concede that birds have some taste sensations, and one investigator suggests that they are sensitive to the same taste qualities as we are [26]. But eating so often "on the run," they depend considerably on vision. There is not time to sample on every occasion the red and yellow berries and continue with the one they prefer. If the red ones have been satisfactory in past experience, then the red color is a sufficient cue for eating. The fact that some species will eat bitter things such as ants does not necessarily indicate insensitivity. Actually, they may enjoy bitter qualities more than we do. Some insects may be "distasteful" to birds—at least they are avoided—but on the whole we have very little detailed knowledge about taste sensations of birds.

It is much the same story with reference to the sense of smell, and experimental results are meager and contradictory. For instance, the classic experiment with vultures found that though they would not approach a carcass that was covered, they were attracted to a large picture of the carcass and even tried to eat the picture. Then there was the case of the black vulture that tackled a skunk although the latter was using his not-so-secret weapon. On the other hand, a recent study with turkey vultures used containers filled with leaves, some having meat concealed under the leaves. Two captive vultures selected the containers with the food in preference to the other containers a significant number of times [21].

Tests with turkey vultures in the wild again gave positive results. A stuffed mule-deer specimen positioned in an open field to look like a dead animal failed to attract the birds on five successive days, but a fresh deer carcass in the same spot got results. It was noted also that the vultures instead of circling above the animal circled about 100 yards downwind [30]. With black vultures, however, results were negative in similar tests.

Smell might conceivably be more important for ground-dwelling birds. The kiwi, a flightless bird of New Zealand, has nostrils at the end of the bill and thus is able to locate worms in the dark as it probes in the ground. In one experiment worms were buried in some pails of sand but not in others, and the kiwi was able to smell them out [23, p. 36]. Then there is the anecdote of a boat laying a trail of animal fat on the ocean and an albatross picking up the trail, presumably responding to the odor, although we cannot be absolutely certain.

Perhaps a safe conclusion from all this would be that while some birds undoubtedly have a sense of smell, this sense is, on the whole, poorly developed in birds.

Touch

The sense of touch has considerable utility for some birds. The snipe and woodcock, probing deep in the mud with a long bill, are supposed to detect food by tactual contact. Young birds in the nest respond to a silent jarring of the nest by opening their mouths for food, presumably because the touch sense organs are involved. The jarring is originally caused by the parent with a food supply alighting on the nest before the nestlings' eyes are open. Later on they open their mouths when they see the parent, but if the nest is jarred when the parent is not visible, they crouch in apparent fear.

Another possible instance of response to touch was the parent thrush reported to have acted peculiarly just before the egg hatched. She hopped to the rim of the nest, poked at the egg, flew away, returned with a worm and tried to feed the egg. Something triggered this premature behavior. It is possible that the chick was moving inside the egg and the parent, being in close contact, could feel this activity through the shell. It is also possible that some sound from the egg was involved.

Temperature

Temperature is sensed by the skin in a manner similar to touch. Birds evidently detect changes in temperature. It is one of the variables in the weather pattern that may set them off on a migratory flight although other stimuli are also involved. Under controlled conditions, responses to temperature can be noted. During their first few days of life, chicks do a great deal of distress calling, but they do so more often at temperatures of 60 degrees F. than of 110 degrees F. [14].

Equilibrium

Finally, there are the sensations that help to control equilibrium, though these are often taken for granted in the case of birds. A person with a defective sense of equilibrium may get along, after a fashion, by taking hold of objects and by watching the position of things about him; for instance, whether the telephone poles tip or appear straight up. But in free flight, a bird cannot do this. Little organs inside the ear provide sense of balance, and birds certainly have them. Interestingly enough, they are better developed anatomically in birds like swallows, which fly practically all the time, than in ducks, which spend much time swimming.

Critical Part of Stimulus

Up to this point we have noted that birds are well equipped to receive stimuli—many of them—from the outer world, but the bird cannot respond to everything at once. Some parts of a situation may be more significant than others so that he can neglect the latter with impunity. Let us take a few examples and see what actually triggered the action.

Adults / An adult robin with a mouthful of insects returns to a nest of young birds. What it reacts to is the reddish insides of the mouths—not the fuzzy bodies, the minor sounds or the sticks in the nest. This fact was demonstrated when an observer wanted to collect some of the insects for study. Using a nursing-bottle nipple and a pair of scissors bent appropriately, he made a device resembling a nestling's open mouth and painted it red. The nest was in a nestling box with a perch outside the entrance on which the adult bird always paused before entering. The observer was concealed in a blind close by but could extend his arms outside to reach the nest box. He dropped a screen across the entrance to the box as the bird approached and presented the imitation mouth. Thereupon the bird popped the insects into the rubber contraption. Obviously the red mouth was the part of the situation to which the parent bird was reacting. The color of the mouth varies with different species but apparently is effective for parents of that particular species. One type of swift even has large conspicuous spots on the roof of the mouth to enhance the target value. But species that are not fed in the nest lack the conspicuous mouth interior. It is not needed.

After young birds leave the nest, if they are still to be fed by the parent, another stimulus takes over: the hunger call; if the young did not have it, the parent might be unable to locate them.

NESTLINGS / Turning from the stimuli for the parent to those for the young bird, we may consider some species (such as some of the gulls) in which the parent does not put the food into the youngster's mouth at all. The nestling pecks at the parent's bill and takes the food himself. Surprisingly enough, it is the parental bill and not the food that touches off this response, for young gulls will peck at a variety of cardboard models of the parent's bill when presented with no food included. In various experiments young gulls were taken from their nests and studied briefly in a nearby tent that served as a laboratory. Different models of cardboard bills were presented and the number of pecks per minute noted for each model. For herring-gull chicks the most important characteristic of the model was a red spot near the tip of the bill. Provided they had the red patch, cardboard bills of various colors and shapes were effective. Without the red patch, pecking was halfhearted, the actual score being four times as many pecks per minute with the red patch as without it. It was also noted that motion of the model bill helped, although this might have been expected because motion is a basic attention stimulus. Once the chick's attention is drawn to the moving model, it can react to the red patch.

With another species (the laughing gull) in a similar study, the inclusion of the head in the model appeared more important than was the case with the herring gull. Also, the shape of the bill was more significant—a long slim bill was effective, while a rounded one tended to produce confusion. Here again we see that some limited part of the situation was the actual stimulus to which the bird reacted [12].

DANGER OVERHEAD / Another situation in which birds have to observe selectively occurs when, with other birds flying overhead, it is necessary to react differently according to whether it is a friend or a foe above. In some cases the mere silhouette of the bird overhead is the effective stimulus, as was demonstrated with young geese, ducks and other fowl in a pen. A cardboard model was used with "wings" extending on each side and with two extensions at right angles to the wings—short in one direction and long in the other. If observed with the short extension in front, the model suggested a hawk with a short neck; with the long extension in front, the model resembled a long necked goose. This seemed to be the way it looked to the bird when the model was towed by string across the area above the pen. If the short end went first, the birds registered alarm as though it were a hawk, but if the long end led, they reacted as they would to a goose, showing no fear [31, p. 49]. Incidentally, a circular disc caused no response.

In other cases, some aspect of the predator's motion was the important stimulus. For instance, a couple of hobbies (small hawks) were flying about and catching insects at a height of about 500 yards with some swallows below them at a height of 200 yards. The swallows did not appear to be disturbed by the hobbies. Presently, however, the hawks stopped hunting insects and began to "play" by swooping rapidly at each other. This greatly alarmed the swallows, which evidently were alert for the rapid swooping motion of a predator that usually meant danger.

Again, some shorebirds walking in the water panicked when a gull or another large shorebird not an actual predator dropped swiftly from the sky. This rapid drop, so much like the dive of a falcon after a shorebird, evidently was the effective cue to which the shorebirds reacted. Such reaction would, on occasion, be a lifesaver [31, p. 41].

To cite one more instance, a redstart (warbler) was observed to seize by the anterior end the larvae it ate. One might suspect that the bird would observe the larva moving forward and pick it up by the end that got there first. However, the same thing happened when the larvae did not move. There was a brown spot near the front end of the larvae that evidently was the real cue. This was corroborated by painting an additional brown spot on the rear end, in which case the redstart selected the rear end about as often as the front [8].

Tendencies to react to a specific part of a stimulus situation like those just described presumably were developed in the rough course of evolution and are innate. It is possible, however, to teach an individual bird to react to some detailed aspects. Pigeons in the laboratory were taught to watch a voltmeter and, when the meter was at the high end of the scale, to peck at a little target that brought a food reward. But to develop and set such a response in the species would, of course, take hundreds of years and many voltmeters [36].

Cues such as we have been discussing work satisfactorily in situations where the bird normally encounters them. But mistakes may occur in a different situation where the limited cue is not enough. The British robin, when defending his territory from an intruding robin, assumes a threatening posture. Evidently he recognizes the intruder by the reddish color, for he may assume the threatening posture at a bundle of red feathers or even a piece of red cloth. One robin reacted to some tomatoes ripening in a window. No harm resulted in these cases except wasted effort, but it showed that while alertness to red takes care of the territory situation, it is inappropriate elsewhere. The inflexibility of these inborn tendencies is sometimes unfortunate as in the case of a bird that normally scoops a hollow in some gravel for a nest but selects a site only a few inches from a highway.

Recognition

Mistakes / Some of the examples just cited are actually cases of recognition. This is a mechanism that humans also have, and it gets more dramatic perhaps when we make a mistake and slap the wrong person on the back. We notice the glasses and the moustache but neglect other parts of the physiognomy—hence our mistake. And so it goes with birds in recognizing adults of their own species.

The male flicker, for instance, has a black "moustache" on the side of the face. A female flicker was caught and a similar marking was glued to her cheek. When released, she went to the nesting hole that she and her mate had been digging in a tree. The male attacked her as an intruder. She was recaptured and once the moustache was removed, everything reverted to the *status quo ante bellum*. Evidently the black mark on the cheek was the all-important item in recognizing sex. Almost identical results were found using a yellowthroat (warbler), the male of which has a conspicuous black domino or mask on the cheek area. An artificial one placed on the female broke up the family temporarily, just as it did with the flickers [23, p. 121].

Again, when the heads of female mourning doves in an aviary were colored with airplane paint, it ruined the family relationship. The erstwhile mate stopped the kind of coos normally made around "home" and gave forth the sound associated with mere perching [9].

Importance of the head / These instances suggest that it is the head of the bird that is most important in recognition. Some other examples bring out this same point. Woodpeckers (European species) attacked a stuffed dummy of the same species that was placed near their nest during the incubation period. When it fell to the ground and the head separated from the body, they attacked the head but ignored the headless body [4].

Domestic chickens in a flock develop a sort of hierarchy wherein one individual dominates all the others, another is second in order and so on. This is called the peck order and will be discussed in detail in a later chapter. Observers of such flocks noted that cues connected with the head were the most important in recognizing individuals for the purpose of conforming to peck order. By experimentally changing aspects of the head, such as the comb, shifts in dominance could be produced artificially [11].

AUDITORY CUES / These cues play a part in recognition as when we recognize a person by his voice on the telephone. An olive-backed thrush attacked a model of its own species introduced into its territory and continued the attack when a recording of the song of an olive-backed thrush was played. However, if a song recording of some other species of thrush was played when the olive-backed thrush model was introduced, there was no attack. The auditory aspect said "friend" and the visual "foe," with the first aspect dominant in this case. It is not safe to generalize that auditory cues are always more important than visual, although they certainly play a role.

There was a case reported of a song sparrow listening to a recording of another song sparrow's song with no model in sight. The bird attacked the loudspeaker from which the song emanated, evidently regarding it as an intruder or enemy. Incidentally, the experimenter was using a commercial record of birdsongs and an announcer's voice said, "Song sparrow," just preceding the song. After a number of repetitions of the experiment the bird did not wait for the song but attacked the loudspeaker at the announcement "Song sparrow."

RECOGNIZING YOUNG / Some birds have problems even in recognizing their own young. With the average song bird the problem is not serious because the young are confined to the nest for many days and the parent merely needs to recognize its own nest, but difficulties arise when cowbirds are present. Cowbirds are parasitic, always laying their eggs in other birds' nests. The parent bird in charge of the nest sometimes recognizes the foreign eggs and pushes them out, but more often it hatches the cowbird's eggs along with its own. Then the trouble begins. If the parents could recognize the intruders they could let them starve, but the bird is unable to make this recognition—at least at this stage—and continues to feed the young cowbirds, often at the expense of its own brood, for the cowbird makes more noise and opens its mouth wider.

The problem is more obvious in the case of colony-nesting seabirds whose nests are close together. Some species of terns appear to be unable to recognize their own eggs or newly hatched chicks, but by the time the chicks are two days old, the parents can recognize them by their voices. Fortunately this is before the young begin to wander from the nest for later, when a number of adults and young move around or migrate together, each adult appears to feed only one or two young, presumably its own [5].

It is the same story with herring gulls. They will feed strange youngsters as well as their own until the age of two days. Thereafter they will attack and even kill young birds that intrude [32, p. 33]. Coots are a little slower in recognizing their own young, taking close to two weeks [1]. In two species of albatross, the figure is about ten days [28].

With penguins the situation is a bit equivocal. They often have a crèche with numerous youngsters supervised by a few adults while most of the parents go off to the water periodically and bring back food. In one species, as far as could be observed, the returning parents fed the young in the crèche indiscriminately [24, p. 97]. On the other hand several other species of penguin showed indications that sometimes they do feed their own young. In indiscriminate feeding, the larger and more aggressive chicks attract more attention and get most of the food. Nevertheless in some colonies the smaller ones are fed and survive. Presumably their own parents did this, although we cannot be absolutely sure. Even in the case first mentioned, it is possible that a parent could recognize its own young but did not bother with them when everybody was feeding everybody.

Enemies / Birds may be called upon to recognize predators. We have already mentioned the ducks and geese reacting to the shape of the silhouette towed overhead, which, basically, involved recognition. In other cases it has been noted that the predator must be moving to be an effective stimulus. Swallows could differentiate dangerous and harmless species when in flight but not when the predator was sitting still [19].

Motion / In one case it seemed that the birds responded to the motion alone, neglecting other aspects, and thus made a mistake in recognition. Purple martins dive-bombed model airplanes with a purple and yellow pattern. No enemy or predator of that color and design could have come within the bird's experience or that of his ancestors. Apparently the motion was the cue for enemy.

Alternative explanations might be either a tendency to attack any strange object or undue belligerence on the part of the particular birds observed, as we shall note later that individual birds often differ in personality characteristics. It could, of course, have been mere "play," similar to the way some swallows swoop at each other with no apparent ulterior objective. This highlights again the limitations of a psychologist in interpreting behavior of an organism that cannot talk about it [25].

Here is a still more tricky case for interpretation A captive starling was fed from a dish. When allowed to fly freely, it acted as if it were catching an insect in the air, swooping, seeming to catch, and going through the motions of swallowing. Did the starling actually have a hallucination and manipulate an imaginary insect or did the observer stretch things a bit in his interpretation [13]?

SOUNDS / Another case is that of a female ruffed grouse that came out of the brush when the motor of a tractor was started. Possibly she was after insects or worms stirred up by the tractor, but presently she ran right up to the tractor and could even be picked up. It was suggested that the motor put out sounds that suggested a male grouse's drumming.

In a similar but more serious situation certain sounds in the spectrum of an airplane (Electra) were found to resemble the chirp of field crickets. A few years ago at the Boston airport numerous starlings, being interested in crickets, rose in the air just before an Electra took off. The plane zoomed through the flock and sucked some starlings into the scoop, which killed the engine and caused the plane to crash [2].

Another serious case (at least for the nestling) involved a parent bird that was cleaning up the nest and discarding foreign material, as many species do routinely. Somebody had recently banded the young birds. When the parent saw a leg band, obviously strange and "foreign" material, she picked it up and dropped it over the edge of the nest. The fact that there was a leg within the band and a young bird attached to the leg made no difference. The parent was reacting only to a limited part of the situation—the strange object—and figuring out the consequences to the family was too complicated [32, p. 332].

PEOPLE / How about birds recognizing people? Many animals, of course, do this—dogs, for example. One instance involving a bird is reported by a reliable observer. A male mockingbird repeatedly attacked a woman when she approached the nest and would actually strike her on the back. "More than once the bird singled me out for an attack as I stood with others in the vicinity of the nest," she said [16]. No further study was made of the actual cues for recognition such as costume but at least some cues were adequate. The writer visited a family that kept a pet crow in a cage. Whenever he approached, the crow tried to attack him through the wire. When other persons approached, there was no attack. It might have been because the writer was a stranger or he may have annoyed the crow somehow at the outset, for actually he disliked the crow. At any rate the crow proved he could make a selective recognition.

EGGS / A final item that birds sometimes need to recognize is their own eggs. When a ground-nesting bird's egg rolls out the nest, it should be rolled back. There are many anecdotes about a bird trying to incubate some foreign object such as a doorknob, but there have been a few systematic efforts to substitute various "eggs" in order to observe the bird's behavior. A greylag goose, in a situation where occasionally an egg rolls from the nest, was given a cylinder and rolled it back to the nest and behaved similarly with an artificial egg much larger than normal. Evidently size and shape were not critical cues [34, p. 57]. With herring gulls the shape of the egg likewise was unimportant, but when the markings were varied deliberately, the tendency either to retrieve or neglect the egg was enhanced. If the specks on the shell were smaller, darker and more contrasting, there was more favorable consideration, and larger size was also favored [3]. Obviously there are species differences in the egg characteristics that are effective for recognition. There may also be differences between species in general ability to recognize eggs, whatever the characteristics.

TIME

THE bird's world has another variable to which it may be necessary for them to make some adjustment, namely, time. True, they are not as tied to the clock as humans are with office arrival at nine and lunch at noon, and it may be that certain "timed" behavior actually involves response to other cues such as waking at daylight or heading for the roost at sunset.

We might preface our discussion with an incident that demonstrates the need for care in interpreting behavior as related to time. Some birds in the Luxembourg Gardens in Paris used to gather at 9:45 A.M. at a point where a visitor fed them regularly. Though many came from an area from which they could not see the person approach, they arrived nevertheless at the correct time. Presently, when the area changed to Daylight Time, the birds adjusted immediately, arriving an hour earlier by suntime. This caused some uncritical speculation as to how they got the word. Were they reading a big clock in the vicinity? Presently it was discovered that they took their cue from workmen in the Gardens, who went on the job at 9:45 on either kind of time.

There are situations in which the bird reacts in some fashion to time with no obvious external cue. A bird flies into the brush to escape a predator and does not emerge immediately. It waits an appropriate length of time and may have some genetic tendency to do so, but in the process it must have some awareness of a lapse of time. We shall see later that, in the course of migration and especially in navigation of their flights, birds use some kind of "biological clock," the actual nature of which is not known.

In the laboratory it can be shown that birds are able to perceive fairly short time intervals. Pigeons were placed in a chamber on the wall of which was a round plastic key that could be illuminated. They were taught to peck this key when it was lighted to receive a bit of grain as a reward. Then the real experiment began. The key would be alternately dark and light, but the dark intervals were 3 seconds, 6 seconds, 9, 12 and so on up to 30, and these different time intervals occurred in random order. The bird was now rewarded only when the preceding dark interval was three seconds. When they pecked at the lighted key after any other dark interval, nothing happened. The question was whether or not the pigeons could learn to peck only after the three-second dark interval, that is, basically whether or not they could distinguish a three-second interval from the others. It developed that they could do this in a way—at least they would peck most frequently after the three-second darkness, and to some extent after six or nine seconds, but seldom after the longer intervals. One bird, for instance, in a complete session pecked 625 times for the three-second darkness, 440 times for the six-second, 240 for the nine-second, and around 100 for the remainder. He certainly perceived the difference between short and long intervals and came pretty close to selecting the three-second interval. Three other pigeons showed the same trend, although not quite so strikingly. In other series of tests the birds were rewarded after the longest interval (30 seconds) rather than the shortest. Similar results were obtained [27].

A study with starlings in a somewhat similar situation brought out their ability to discriminate intervals of about four hours. They were put in a cage where pecking at a small target brought food much as in the case of the pigeons just discussed, the food coming only at 6 A.M., 10 A.M., 2 P.M. and 6 P.M. Although the birds could peck at any time, they were rewarded at only those four periods. All pecking throughout the day was recorded automatically with pens on a moving tape. The birds pecked now and then throughout the day, but the graphic record showed definite peaks beginning 10 to 15 minutes in advance of the critical time they actually would receive the food. Somehow they were able to perceive that it was "about time" for food. They did not waste much effort in pecking during the four-hour periods when no food would be available.

The bird has a lot of equipment for getting information from the world around him, and he is somewhat selective in receiving this information. In a general way he perceives the things that are important to him. Our next question is what he then does about it?

CHAPTER III

The Major Drives and Motives

General Nature

Stimuli, as we noted in the previous chapter, enter the birds' sense organs. Then what? Nothing, perhaps, unless some drive or motive is present. The cedar waxwings sit in our shrubbery and merely look at the berries, but presently the hunger drive takes over and they begin to eat. When they are satiated the drive is reduced and the birds go elsewhere. Some drives may be regarded in a way as internal stimuli—contraction of the stomach muscles or dryness of tissues in the mouth and throat—but at least hunger and thirst facilitate certain behaviors. Again, the cardinal shows little interest in the opposite sex as such in midwinter but the drive comes back with the spring; the males are singing lustily before the snow is gone.

These factors give a sort of direction to behavior—toward food or safety, for instance—and although much behavior of man or beast is goal-directed, something has to provide that direction and keep things going. At the level of birds, these factors generally are called drives; at some higher levels, especially with humans, we speak of them as motives. The difference is largely one of complexity so that we shall not make too sharp a distinction in our discussion, but the higher we go in the scale, the more tricky the interpretation sometimes gets. We press the knob on the drinking fountain in direct response to the thirst drive, but children may press the same knob when they are not thirsty at all just to make it squirt or, better still, to wet someone—obviously a different motive. We are less likely to encounter difficulties like this in interpreting bird behavior. The basic drive generally is the whole story and is obvious.

A characteristic that contributes to the over-all effectiveness of drives is the way their intensity changes, with resulting change in the vigor of response. A bird flies faster than usual when chased, especially if the predator is speedy. With a more complicated act like building a nest, normally about a six-day job for a pair of robins, let us suppose the almost completed nest is destroyed when the eggs are about ready to be laid (internal stimulus or drive). The birds will rebuild the nest in one day. Again, experiments with laboratory animals running through a maze to obtain a food reward show that they run more rapidly after 24 hours without food than after a fast of only 12 hours. Birds have not been tried in this particular experimental situation but animal psychologists have done it with so many other vertebrates that they believe this principle works all up and down the animal scale. We humans show similar tendencies, of course. We go out the back door at a moderate pace "to get some fresh air," but if the house is on fire our response to the stronger drive will obviously be more vigorous. The strength of the drive varies with the need.

Food

Let us turn now to some of the major drives of birds. Food is one of the most obvious and important—if the bird does not eat, it does not survive. The hunger drive leads adult birds to forage and nestlings to yell for food, some of the latter doing so even after they leave their nests, as described earlier. They enjoy a prolonged childhood just as some humans do. One might get the erroneous impression that the food drive and the resulting eating is a continuous process. Although the sparrows seem to be at the feeder all day long, it may not be the same birds involved all of that time. An ornithologist thought that he had a single pair of cardinals inhabiting his yard, until he started trapping cardinals to put colored bands on their legs so he could identify them. It developed that his "pair of cardinals" comprised 14 different birds. Therefore the continuous presence of sparrows at the feeder just mentioned presumably represented different groups operating in relays.

This is not to minimize the food requirements of birds and the importance of the hunger drive. Metabolism is quite rapid, and young birds particularly eat an amazing amount in proportion to their size; in fact, some nestlings must eat half their body weight per day just to stay alive, to say nothing of growing. On occasion birds may take on a lot of fuel in the form of food and resulting fat deposits, like the warbler that is about to fly nonstop across the

Gulf of Mexico. It devotes several days to swallowing insects, and the drive must be unusually vigorous at that time. It is part of the migration pattern. We shall discuss later the variables that actually trigger the migration.

AMOUNT OF FOOD / The food drive keeps the bird eating until satiated, but that is not the whole story. Psychological factors enter the situation. For one thing, the eating may be influenced by the amount of food presented. Some hens after fasting for 24 hours ate from piles of grain. When the pile was large, they ate about 33 grams more than when they ate from a small pile, although the latter was adequate for all they could possibly eat [3]. Similarly, chickens in a four-foot runway with rice visible at the end ran down the runway faster if they saw six grains at the end rather than only one grain [9]. Another experiment showed that the number of "pieces" was more important than the gross amount. A grain of corn cut into four parts gave more drive than a single grain before it was cut [16]. Probably the four pieces separated a bit and covered a larger area, thus giving an impression of greater magnitude. We could scarcely expect the bird to estimate the separate volumes and total them, but the fact remains that the real or apparent amount of food present influences the drive. Conceivably this is just another case of a more intense stimulus producing a more vigorous response. For instance, the sudden sound of a door slamming makes us jump, but at the sound of an explosion, we jump farther. Anyway, the demonstrated relation for birds between size of "portion" and food drive leads one to speculate about humans and what determines the amounts we eat.

SOCIAL FACILITATION / Another factor which may influence the strength of the drive has been called "social facilitation." Many animals engaged in some activity alone perform differently than when another animal is present and engaged in the same activity. In the present context we are concerned with one bird eating in the presence of another eater. For instance, a hen was observed which ate until satiated and would eat no more. When a hungry hen was introduced into the pen with the satiated one, the latter resumed eating and consumed an additional 67 per cent of what it had eaten on the first round. Obviously it had not exhausted its eating potential at the outset and could, if properly stimulated, eat much more. The presence of another eater was what did the trick [3]. Similarly, isolated and paired chicks were weighed after a 12-hour period on their second, third and fourth days of life. On all three days the paired chicks ate more than the isolated ones. Social facilitation operates quite early in life [14]. This principle has been given a practical turn in fattening hogs where the social stimulus has auditory as well as visual components.

This mechanism may enhance the food drive for birds in situations where it is not so obvious. If a good source of food is available somewhere, a lot of birds converge upon it simultaneously, and it is quite possible that they eat somewhat more under those circumstances because of this facilitation than they would if they came upon the food individually. In one instance, cormorants were observed to fish more actively when they were in a group [4]. Social facilitation is not the same thing as cooperation in getting the food. In some instances birds actually help each other. For instance, pelicans form a circle and chase fish toward the center of the circle, where everybody can get at them.

In passing it may be noted that social facilitation may operate on other drives beside food. Some species have been observed to fly faster on the average when migrating than under ordinary circumstances, as we shall see. The presence of others flying alongside a bird may have a facilitating effect. However the whole process of migration, with some of its overtones in the way of glandular changes, may do some facilitating in its own right. Perhaps both factors are involved in the speed-up.

THIRST

CLOSELY related to the food drive is thirst. The drive operates less frequently and less dramatically. No experimental study as far as birds are concerned has been reported as yet, but thirst is an important drive and without it birds would become dehydrated and obviously in bad shape, especially species that eat dry food such as seeds.

Temperature

There is a drive to maintain a constant temperature or to "get in out of the cold" as it were, even though feathers make pretty good insulation. When a cold wind is blowing, we find more birds on the sheltered side of the woods. In winter we sometimes find starlings perched on chimneys, presumably taking advantage of some of the warmth that is transmitted up the flue. It has also been suggested that they might be getting the smoke into their feathers as a means of controlling parasites. However, studies have been made by counting the number of starlings on chimneys in a specific area on cold days and warm days and it worked out that the number was conclusively related to the temperature.

Roosts / We find large numbers of birds roosting together in winter, and they usually select a patch of evergreen trees for this purpose because there is more shelter in evergreens. However, the writer knows of one roost of a half million blackbirds in a small group of deciduous trees, where there were no leaves to protect them during the cold weather. The woods must have been selected for some other reason. For that matter, there are instances where the birds apparently do not seek escape from the cold at all, as in Detroit, where starlings have roosted in winter on the metal structures of river bridges. Here they were completely exposed to the wind, cold and storm, with absolutely no shelter at all, so that while the drive usually brings them into a more comfortable situation, they can on occasion "take it."

Fear-Escape

Escaping from danger is another drive that is basic to survival. Presumably it involves fear of a dangerous object or animal such as a predator. The bird, recognizing the predator, gets under cover or out of range in time. (We have already mentioned in Chapter II the recognition aspect in this connection such as whether the silhouette overhead resembles a goose or a hawk and whether the object sails or swoops.) With their keen vision, birds are able to make these necessary recognitions, hopefully before it is too late. Species differ in how they handle the situation from that point.

Small birds are likely to dash into bushes too dense for a large predator such as a hawk to follow. If the threat is from the ground (a cat), they fly upward and away. One of the main considerations in location of a bird feeder or a birdbath is to place it relatively near to cover so that the birds can hide promptly. While we may not have many hawks flying over our backyards, nevertheless the birds seem alert to such possibilities and presumably feel more comfortable in any feeder near adequate cover. On the other hand, the feeder should not be too close to the shrubbery—it should be more than one cat-jump distant so the birds cannot be ambushed from the ground.

This drive to get away from danger is not always completely specific as to the stimulus that touches it off. Any large moving object or sound of unknown origin may be sufficient to initiate this response. In case of doubt, it is just as well for the bird to play it safe. Although it may annoy the Audubon party carrying nothing more lethal than binoculars when someone inadvertently slams a car door, in the long run more ducks will survive if the escape drive operates under any equivocal circumstances.

Sex

This is the drive which contributes primarily to the continuation of the species. With the male bird the drive begins before the female is in the picture at all, since the initial drive comes from hormones—certain secretions of the sex glands. Postmortem studies reveal cyclical changes in the glands with enlargement occurring at the appropriate time. This role of the glands can be demonstrated further by injecting young birds with the appropriate hormone. The result is precocious sex behavior [10]. Injecting the wrong hormone in females makes them behave somewhat like males.

The first objective manifestation by the male occurs when he sets up his territory. He does this in an appropriate area with consideration of such things as trees, grass or food facilities. Then from a perch, for hours on end, he announces to the world that this is *his* territory. That is what his vigorous singing is all about; he is advertising his presence and warning other males to keep away, even though this is not done in so many words. It is risky even to discuss "vocabulary," but at least the other males keep away, for the most part, and any intruder is chased away.

Presently a female comes along. About then the drive enters a second phase somewhat on the order of courtship, the ritual varying with different species. The song continues and by itself may be totally convincing to the female; but often there is posturing—holding the head in peculiar fashion, flashing wings, presenting the female with bits of grass (nesting material). The penguin presents his lady with a small rock (their kind of nesting material). Some males strut or do an elaborate "dance".

This behavior leads to the mating, which may be transitory or forever. At about this point they go about the business of building a nest as part of the same drive. Materials and construction vary with the species, of course, and draw on instinctive factors. Then eggs are laid and incubated till they hatch; both parents may take turns on the nest or one alone may sit on the eggs. Then the young must be fed—plentifully—and also protected from danger even after they have left the nest.

Somewhere along the line the drive shifts from the purely sexual to something more "parental." It may be just a difference in emphasis, remaining part of the same basic tendency. In some species such as ducks, where the young are able to run about almost as soon as hatched, these later stages are abbreviated. At any rate, without this drive there would not be any birds to speak of in a couple of years. More *family* details will be discussed in Chapter IX.

Migration

The same hormones we have just been discussing are involved in another important project—migration. The male bird, partly as a result of glandular development, may be feeling the urge to set up his territory, but the appropriate territory is 500 miles to the north. There is only one thing to do: migrate. Involved in all this are probably many other factors, for things seem to happen at about the right time; the bird does not fly north in January or wait till August.

There are two ways to get information as to what really happens. One approach is postmortem examination of the glands themselves, with special reference to size and the cyclical changes through the year [15]. The other is systematic observation of "migratory restlessness." This can best be done with birds in an aviary or a large, preferably circular, cage. Perches are arranged all around the edge, with each perch wired so that when a bird alights on it a circuit is closed and a pen records it on a moving tape. When the migration season approaches, the birds normally become restless and fly about the cage more than usual. Moreover, if it is the season when the species ordinarily migrates in a northerly direction, the captive birds go in that direction as far as they can, the tape indicating that perching is primarily on the north side of the cage.

It is suspected that an important factor in bringing about the migratory drive is the seasonal changes in the relation between daylight and darkness. This relationship may be controlled artificially if the aviary is indoors with no windows. If in January and February the indoor birds were given the same light/dark schedule they would have had outside, they showed the same glandular development as the control birds outside. But when the light/dark ratio was exaggerated—they would have, say, 14 hours of light rather than the ten hours outside—some bobolinks tested developed migratory restlessness three weeks earlier than the controls that had the normal seasonal amount of light [6]. On the other hand, some white-crowned sparrows that were put on a schedule with shortened periods of daylight in early spring did not show the development of sex glands or gonads normal for that time of year [7].

So it looks as if the lengthening days in late winter and early spring have something to do with setting off the migration. But we also need *decreasing* amounts of light relative to darkness some months prior to that—analogous to the shortening days in October and November. If the indoor birds were on a decreasing light/dark schedule in the autumn, things worked out normally the following spring. An increasing light/dark ratio in the fall interfered with the usual glandular development some months later. Evidently the shortening days of autumn provide a necessary preparatory phase or refractory period without which the increasing daylight in spring cannot do its job. It is as if the glands could not be pushed too fast and the mechanism needed a rest period [2].

The matter is complicated and is the subject of considerable current research. There is even some question as to the role of the pituitary gland, which acts on both the thyroid and the gonads. In one case where the gonads were removed but the pituitary was intact, the birds still showed migratory restlessness at the right time [12]. There seems to be some agreement that the pituitary is the basic factor but usually works through the gonads. At any rate, it seems pretty well established that the light/dark changes do influence some of the glandular mechanisms, which in turn trigger the migration tendency [5, p. 314].

When the drive reaches that point at which the birds are ready to take off, favorable weather conditions provide the final touch, but a strong head wind, for example, will temporarily delay the exodus.

In the autumn migration, when there is no breeding in immediate prospect, the weather plays a larger role. It gets colder as winter approaches and the insects die off to the discomfiture of insect eaters. We know less about fall migration, for it has not been studied as systematically. The matter will be considered further in Chapter V, because we are mainly concerned here with the basic drives involved.

Curiosity

Curiosity is a drive that is not as important or as pronounced as some of the others we have been discussing. Nor does it loom as large in bird behavior as in that of some other kinds of animals; for example, monkeys, which will spend hours looking through a peephole into a laboratory where people are working. But birds, too, sometimes show curiosity. The everyday instance is manifest as they gather at the distress call of one of their own or some other species. Suppose a robin being banded gives loud and long protests. Practically all the robins in the neighborhood gather within 20 feet of the operation. Sometimes blue jays come along also. We are not quite sure what is back of this. Some of it may be a readiness to drive away some "enemy" that is causing the distress of the vocalist, but some of it is probably just curiosity as to the source of the sound.

However, distress calls do not always operate to attract curious birds. On the contrary, sometimes the birds depart in alarm. If one wishes to make a census of the number of red-winged-blackbird nests in a field of alfalfa, the best procedure is to play a few recordings of red-wing distress calls at a rather high volume. Every female in the alfalfa field within hearing will pop up from her nest in apparent alarm and can be counted before she settles back. If recordings of this sort are played near a roost of "blackbirds," many of them will leave the roost temporarily.

Pests / This is as good a place as any to mention the use of recorded distress calls in the control of "pests." Some birds, notably starlings, are just that around some of our cities, where they roost on downtown buildings, especially those with convenient ledges, or take over a group of trees in a residential neighborhood. Their presence has implications with reference to aesthetics, sanitation, dry cleaning, car washing and citizen morale.

The fact that they may flee in alarm at a distress call has led to the hope that they may be driven permanently from an area. What usually happens is that they leave momentarily and then return. If the alarm procedure is repeated night after night they become accustomed to it.

Effective control by this method, definitely not an amateur job, might proceed somewhat as follows: Preliminary study is made of light intensities as related to the birds' gathering in order to time the presentation correctly. Usually the birds come into a main roost from several preroosts, which must be located. The first night, when the main roost is about full, play the record till most of the birds leave and then stop. After most of them have returned, play it again till they leave, and keep repeating this procedure till dark. The second night proceed as on the first. On the third and succeeding nights go to the preroosts and frighten them there, then come to the main roost for the usual program. Perhaps after five nights or so the main roost will be pretty well abandoned. There will still remain the problem of where they go from your roost. Maybe they will pick a site a few blocks distant, making the problem there as bad as ever, although with different constituents. Some cities install large traps and liquidate thousands of starlings, for this species is not protected by law. Even so there may be a large reserve population not too far away so that the inroads on the roost will not be as large as hoped for [8].

If we return to the curiosity drive, another instance is the routine practice of bird watchers of producing squeaks by kissing the back of the hand vigorously, a sound that may resemble distress calls of a sort. At any rate, birds of several species are sufficiently curious to appear from the shrubbery or undergrowth where they were concealed. The method works better if the bird watcher himself is partly concealed. Kinglets and chickadees are especially susceptible to these sounds.

Measurement of Drives

It would be interesting if we could measure some of the drives and determine their comparative strength, as has been done with some animals. In one experiment a hungry rat was placed on one side of an electric grid and food on the other side. He could cross the grid to get the food by taking the electric shock involved, and it was possible to vary the degree of hunger and the amount of shock to calibrate, in a way, the food drive versus the electrical deterrent. For instance, how many volts would he take in order to get the food after a 12-hour or a 16-hour fast? No study of this sort has been made with birds. Also, it would be possible to extend the experiment described earlier that measured the amount eaten in relation to the amount of food provided. We could systematically vary the amount of available food in successive trials and note the additional increments eaten; or, as in the other experiment where the bird ran toward food placed at the end of a runway, we could time his speed accurately and relate it to the amount of food at the end in a series of experiments. This might give us some notion as to the strength of the drive in a particular case or with a number of individual birds.

Another possible source of data might involve the "goal-gradient" principle. This is the tendency for an animal to work harder or go faster as it approaches the goal. Rats, in going through a maze to get food at the end, run faster as they get nearer to the end. Something of this sort was found with robins on migration from their winter quarters in Louisiana to their breeding grounds in Alaska. Enough banded birds were recovered at various locations to afford some notion as to their speed at various parts of the trip. From Louisiana to southern Minnesota the birds averaged about 13 miles per day. In southern Canada they accelerated to 30 miles per day, but by the time they reached Central Canada they covered 52 miles daily. When they actually reached Alaska, they were doing 70 miles per day. The drive increased as they approached the goal. This was a very crude measurement of the strength of a drive, but it is about the only report in quantitative terms for birds.

Conflict of Drives

At the human level, drives or motives sometimes conflict. The student may want to study and also go to the theater; or a person is torn between watching a television program and doing a jigsaw puzzle. Such conflicts can become quite severe and even emotionally upsetting until eventually one drive prevails. And so it goes with birds. They frequently have such conflicts, but we are apt to notice only the cases where the unexpected alternative prevails. For instance, a child was holding a young redstart (warbler) in his hand. This bird had been taken briefly from a nearby nest for photographic purposes. The parent birds were standing by with their mouths full of insects to feed the youngster, but the drive to get away from humans (danger) opposed the drive to feed their young. Presently, however, the male parent actually came over and fed the young bird in the child's hand; with the female parent, the fear prevailed [1, p. 125].

A more dramatic (or at least inconvenient) instance involves the flycatcher in the Galapagos Islands that uses hair in construction of its nest. Sometimes the only hair available is on human heads. The usual drive is to keep away from humans, but at the appropriate season the urge to get hair becomes so great that some of the birds alight on a person's head and try to pull out some hair [13, p. 101]. Even though the Galapagos Island birds are noted for their fearlessness, this behavior may be considered rather extreme but there is a species of honeyeater in Australia that does the same thing.

Brain-Stimulation Experiments

Some of the conflicts in drives have been studied by stimulating the drives in the brain. It is possible to plant in the brain tiny electrodes through which voltage (usually not more than two volts) can be applied to some specific brain area. The electrodes are installed with anesthesia, but thereafter are not painful and may be left in place indefinitely. One merely clips wires on them for the duration of an experiment. Some studies of this sort have been made with domestic hens [11].

It is possible to chart different regions of the brain in which stimulation will produce different behaviors. For example, stimulation of a specific region will lead a hen to attack other hens; another region makes her stop eating, spit out the food and shake her head; and still another region leads to flight due to apparent fear. It is an interesting experiment to stimulate two regions simultaneously. For instance one region causes the bird to flatten its feathers and squat down; whereas another area leads it to fluff its feathers. If both areas are stimulated simultaneously, the squatting behavior tends to be suppressed but sometimes the two behaviors are performed in succession. The bird squats a bit and then fluffs its feathers. If the hen receives the stimulation for jumping and fleeing and at the same time is given the stimulation for sitting down, she gets restless and stays sitting for a time but wiggles around and finally jumps.

In only one case reported was the resulting behavior different from either of the behaviors called for by the areas of the brain stimulated. One area leads the bird to peck aggressively and the other area to flee. When both were stimulated simultaneously, the birds screamed and rushed back and forth. Obviously, they were quite upset. This is a bit suggestive of "experimental neuroses" found with some other animals tested. When a rat, say, has to make a choice between a large and a small circle in order to avoid punishment and the difference in size is decreased to the point where he really can't discriminate, he goes into a coma. The bird behavior mentioned above suggests a similar tendency to show some abnormal behavior when there is a major conflict in drives. This, of course, was under laboratory conditions, and whether or not birds have neurotic behavior as a result of the conflicts they encounter in ordinary life we do not know. This experiment gives a little presumption in that direction.

We have noted some of the drives and motives that lead the bird to respond to the stimuli in the world about him. We are now ready to consider some of the actual responses resulting from these drives.

CHAPTER IV

Instinctive Behavior

Nature

The outer world provides stimuli for

the bird, and, impelled by basic drives as we have briefly noted, he does something in response. We shall now consider those responses in more detail. They are of two types: unlearned and learned. The former—reflexes and instincts—are innate and are the subject of the present chapter. The latter result from experience; for example, learning the location of a particular feeder where food is available. They will be discussed later.

Reflexes / Little need be said here about reflex-type behavior. It involves a direct response to simple stimuli like swallowing food that is put in the mouth or winking when an object comes toward the eye. Reflexes operate in all animals that have nervous systems. They do not even require consciousness. We sneeze if we inhale some pollen in our sleep, and we continue breathing under an anesthetic. Some reflexes can take place even without using the brain; the spinal cord is sufficient. A decapitated hen jumps around a bit, and a frog with the head recently removed will pull up the hind legs if touched in the right place on the back. Therefore we can pretty much take the reflexes for granted as far as bird psychology is concerned.

Drives / The discussion of instincts may involve some of the same situations mentioned in the preceding chapter in connection with drives. In general, the drive is the fundamental urge that initiates the process; instinct takes over from there onward. Basic hunger, for example, starts the bird after the food, but foraging for it, storing it or carrying it to the young involves more complicated instinctive behaviors. Again, the basic fear may start the bird away from danger, but instinct determines the direction of escape or the kind of cover used, even leads the bird to pretend injury in order to decoy a predator away from the nest. In the same way, the initial sex urge presently leads to the whole complicated business of setting up territory, getting a mate, building a nest and raising a family.

Role in Birds

Birds depend on their instincts perhaps more than any other vertebrates though insects, of course, are notorious in this respect. Birds are equipped by heredity to handle most life situations. Instincts serve them well for the most part—so well, in fact, that we may erroneously call a behavior rational or intelligent because it seems so well adapted to the ordinary situation. Following a cow across a field in order to eat the insects stirred up by the cow may look like an intelligent inference on the part of the bird; on the contrary, it is part of the instinctive equipment of every cattle egret. Moreover, instincts are often surprisingly inflexible. If a standard food source gives out, some species show a tragic lack of resourcefulness in adapting to other food. If a parent bird, for some reason, cannot reach its own nestlings to feed them, it feeds almost any young bird. An instinctive tendency will sometimes persist when it has outlived its usefulness. Starlings were imported around 1890 and have spread throughout the United States. In Ohio, at least, they still continue to migrate in the original direction of northeast-southwest as their ancestors did in continental Europe, whereas north-south would serve just as well, as it does for other local species. In Europe this direction was favorable for geographical reasons and presumably evolved accordingly. These instinctive tendencies, after all, while generally very effective are rather stereotyped at times.

While instincts play a very large role in birds' lives, even humans are not above instinctive behavior. Watch an irascible person in the line at the ticket window when someone crowds in ahead of him, or note a person whose saddle horse has fallen down with him underneath and his frantic struggle to crawl out from under the horse.

Evolution

These instinctive tendencies evolved through natural selection like many bodily characteristics. Actually, birds evolved originally from reptiles, and the anatomical transition may be seen in some fossil birds of 130 million years ago. Those reptiles with enough feathers to get them off the ground were more likely to survive, and this characteristic was passed along to the offspring. By the same token the tendency to flee in the presence of a swooping predator would have survival value and be passed on to the next generation. Birds who lacked this tendency would soon fall prey and would have no descendants. A nest constructed so that the eggs would not roll out meant that the family was more apt to survive and build similar nests. Birds that dove into the water after fish were more likely to have adequate nourishment and their offspring would follow suit. Multiple examples of this sort could be cited, for that is the way instincts have evolved.

Food Instinct

It is apparent that these instincts have some utility. They serve some biological end such as preserving the individual or preserving the species. Turning to the former, the food instinct is basic and conducive to survival of the individual bird. There are wide variations in the kinds of food consumed by the different species. Some eat seeds or berries, others eat animal matter ranging from mosquitoes to rabbits. We are not especially concerned with the type of food in the present discussion but rather with the different behaviors that are involved in the process of obtaining the food.

Everyone has observed some of the behaviors that go with food getting. Some birds pick up grain from the floor of the feeder or from the ground, some pull worms from the lawn, while others pick at the seed pods of the multiflora roses or the cherries in season. The predators dive after their prey. There seems to be some innate discrimination in the selection of suitable food. Geese of a certain species were observed under laboratory conditions in a room provided with a variety of items sticking through the wall or hanging from the ceiling—such things as wire pipe cleaners and small wads of cloth of different colors. The birds were watched individually from the time of hatching until about 50 hours of age. They tended to peck at items that were high on the wall and those that were light green or yellow, but they avoided items that were placed low and were dark blue. This type of behavior in the wild would tend to direct them toward the seed heads of swamp plants, so obviously they had a built-in tendency to go after the "right" sources of food [6].

Catching insects / Different species of bird have evolved their own characteristic way of catching insects on the wing. The socalled flycatchers like the phoebe or pewee fly out from a perch, snatch up an insect and return to the same perch. The redstart goes out and snaps up the insect but flies to a different perch. The comparative advantage of these alternatives is not clear, but species run pretty true to form in following their own characteristic pattern [8]. A conspicuous feeding behavior is that of the night hawk, which darts around at high speed with its large mouth wide open, accepting any insects that happen to be on its trajectory. It flies through areas where insects are concentrated, uttering a series of nasal calls. This foraging behavior is different from that of the flycatcher, which sees an individual insect and goes after it. The night hawk flies at random and scoops up anything available. Swallows behave similarly.

Foraging in the air is not confined to insects. A falcon, on occasion, dives at smaller birds in flight. Owls and hawks fly or hover in the air or perch high in a tree to locate prey on the ground. When actually diving at the prey in the air, some birds attain a rather high speed, a peregrine falcon (duck hawk) having been clocked at 175 miles per hour in such a power dive [17, p. 62].

Returning to insect hunting, birds do not always find them conveniently in the air at the right time; sometimes they must be flushed from the grass or underbrush. In fact, many insects do not fly at all but merely hop short distances. If a bird just walks through the grass he may disturb some insects, making them fly or hop and thus become available. Sometimes the bird uses supplementary procedures to startle the insects. The mockingbird has conspicuous white bars in its wings and spreads them to flash this white stimulus and thus startle the insects, as has been observed quite frequently in the southern states. When mockingbirds winter in the north, they seldom do this wing flashing. There are no insects available then, and there is no point in trying to flush nonexistent food, so they depend rather on various berries [10]. Detailed observations have been made of the behavior subsequent to the wing flashing. In better than 98 per cent of the cases in some 340 observations, the wing flashing was followed by some aspect of foraging, such as running, hopping, looking down or striking at an insect, indicating an obvious connection [9].

Sometimes instead of flushing the insects itself, the bird relies on someone else to do the job. We have mentioned the cattle egret, which instinctively follows cattle and gobbles up the insects that are flushed by them. On the other hand, an individual bird may learn to do something similar to this. Birds have been known to follow farm machinery to eat worms and other food exposed by the action of the machine. An occasional robin shows interest when a man is spading the garden, but this is a far cry from the instinctive behavior of the egret. It would have required thousands of years of experience around farm machinery for the species to develop an instinctive tendency of that sort.

The turnstone, mentioned previously, pokes its bill under small stones to turn them over, then eats small creatures clinging to the underside.

FISHING / Shorebirds that find some of their food in shallow water have their own methods of flushing it. They stir up the water with their feet and in the process stir up such organisms as sand shrimps, which are more visible when moving than when resting quietly on the bottom. Even small sandpipers have been observed at this behavior [14]. This type of feeding is more common, however, among the larger shorebirds.

The phalarope, which swims around in shallow water and in the process spins vigorously, turns around and around in one spot or does a pattern resembling a figure eight. The motion of the water stirs up the mosquitoe larvae, which the bird eats. This built-in behavior characterizes all phalaropes and, incidentally, helps bird watchers identify phalaropes at a distance.

Some birds go headfirst into the water after their food. Puddle ducks go down just a few inches in shallow water to feed on vegetation on the bottom. They put the front half of their body underwater and leave the other half sticking grotesquely in the air. Other birds dive in deep water after fish. They usually rise in the water, plunge down headfirst and then swim to the desired depth. Some of them go rather deep and stay quite a time. The old squaw duck averages close to a minute underwater, and some scoters and mergansers stay down 45 seconds or more, reappearing with a fish in their mouth if the mission was successful [7].

This instinctive tendency for birds to dive after fish is utilized in one instance by fishermen. In the Far East captive cormorants are employed instead of the usual fishing tackle. A cord is tied around the cormorant's neck so that he cannot swallow and then he is dropped over the side of the boat, another cord keeping him from escaping permanently. Thereupon he goes about his usual business of diving, catching a fish, surfacing and trying in vain to swallow the fish. He is pulled into the boat and induced to disgorge the fish. Then the whole process is repeated. This seems like slave labor, but the cormorant does not seem to resent it and never learns or remembers, going through the routine time after time. Of course, he is allowed enough fish to eat to keep in condition, but this rather "blind" continuance of the activity is characteristic of much instinctive behavior.

Some birds get their fish by diving from the air rather than from the surface of the water. Kingfishers fly along above a creek and when they spy a fish, dive after it. Along the shore of the ocean, terns do much the same thing.

Storage / With some species, storage of the food is part of the instinctive pattern. The Canada jay stores acorns, as does the redheaded woodpecker. The jays have been observed to fill their throats and bills, then fly half a mile into the woods to store the acorns in crevices in trees or in holes made by woodpeckers. In Sweden a species of nutcracker, a large jaylike bird, gathers nuts from lowlands, then flies three or four miles to higher ground and buries the whole mouthful in a hole in the ground. They work at it all day. In winter they manage to dig them up through 18 inches of snow; they have been observed to locate the hiding places under the snow in 86 per cent of their attempts.

While instinctive processes take care of the bulk of food-getting behavior, learning mechanisms do play a part. Learning will be discussed in a later chapter, but, in passing, birds learn the location of a feeder or other source of food. They may even learn to use some new kind of food, as did the birds in England that discovered milk bottles. They had never been brought up on milk but learned to tear off the cap and drink an inch or two. This will also be discussed in more detail elsewhere.

AVOIDING DANGER

LIFE is hazardous for birds. Probably those who die a natural death are in the minority. The unnatural-death rate would be higher if birds did not have some instinctive equipment such as a tendency to escape from danger when it becomes apparent. We have already mentioned how, at the appearance of any strange, moving object or any sudden sound, off they go. We also noted their ability to recognize some specific stimuli as more dangerous than others. It will be recalled that the ducks reacted appropriately according to whether the silhouette overhead resembled a hawk or a goose, while some other species are alert to a rapidly swooping object.

While these tendencies are innate, they are modifiable in specific situations where they serve no useful purpose. The mallard ducks in the aviary were never attacked by the cardboard "hawk" overhead and after 17 days of its flights they were no longer frightened appreciably [13]. Similarly, a chaffinch (British) that instinctively attacked a stuffed owl was subjected to the model owl for 20 minutes a day for five days. There resulted a very pronounced decrease in the aggressive behavior [20, p. 302].

These experiments, however, are not too pertinent to conditions in the wild. Becoming habituated to a predator is impossible unless the predator never attacks. If the bird does not flee every time the predator appears, regardless of its intentions, sooner or later the inevitable happens and that ends the potential habituation.

Even when the danger is not actually visible, birds often exhibit an alertness or a caution that helps to protect them. Quite characteristically, when alighting at a feeder, they take a look around before indulging, and some species take certain precautionary measures when landing on a perch. They pirouette with a quick hop and a 180-degree turn, first one way and then the other, often moving along the perch in this process. Thus they face in several different directions and have a good view of anything suspicious. If they relied on peripheral vision, they might miss something.

This behavior has been observed in redstarts, bay-breasted warblers, gnatcatchers and Baltimore orioles [8]. Similarly, wild ducks and some of the shorebirds circle an area before alighting, evidently alert to possible sources of danger in the area.

Sometimes the potential danger is not a natural predator. It has been suggested that ducklings, for example, learn their fear of people from their parents. Apparently this fear is not a genetic tendency, because wild birds' eggs hatched under domestic birds do not develop a fear of people—it is only when wild parents are involved that this fear develops. If this fear of people were genetic it would have been necessary to have people hunting ducks for countless generations. This has not occurred until comparatively recently and the use of shotguns in the process is still more recent (1, p. 19A). So the ducks have to learn this particular fear from their parents.

Fighting

Instead of fleeing from an object, the bird may attack, the fighting often being tied up with some other instinctive situation. It is seldom that they indulge in fighting merely for its own sake. A common situation of this sort occurs when the male bird is establishing territory for nesting and fighting any intruding males. Another situation involves food, especially if there is a scarcity, but even at a bounteous feeder there may be some commotion. While the contenders usually are of the same species, there are cases where one species attacks another in connection with food. The classic case is the eagle attacking the osprey, which then drops the fish it is carrying.

Fighting is involved in establishing the peck order mentioned earlier. The bird at the top of the hierarchy achieved that position the hard way—by fighting. The arrangement may have some utility in the food situation; instead of everybody fighting at every meal, they establish once and for all who eats first, second and so on.

Quite a bit of bird fighting is just posture rather than actual contact. There is a sort of gesture language, and different species have their characteristic threatening poses. A common posture is rushing forward with wings spread and head extended. This may be sufficient to rout the other party without anyone at all getting clawed. On other occasions, however, there is physical contact with resulting damage and even death, but these cases are in the minority.

Play

Birds frequently indulge in activity that seems to have no utility but appears to be done simply for its own sake. This is what we ordinarily call play. Eider ducks, for example, will ride down a rapid tidal current, walk back across a narrow strip of land and then ride down again. There is no apparent rationale except the sheer "joy of it" [18]. Young kestrels (sparrow hawks) will play with pine cones and grass roots, tossing them about and otherwise manipulating them. Song sparrows engage in what one careful observer called frolic. They do this particularly from the age of 18 to 40 days and occasionally for some time thereafter. The activity involves sudden rapid runs or flights and sharp turns [15, p. 168]. It may be noted that the examples of the Eider ducks and the kestrels involved young birds at play rather than adults. This is interesting in view of the fact that at the human level it is also children who do more of the playing. Perhaps the situation is similar in that the younger birds have fewer duties or responsibilities than the older ones and more available time.

It has been suggested that some play activities actually involve practicing skills that will be important in later life. Young puppies, for example, play roughly with much sparring and pretending to bite, which may be preparation for genuine dogfights next year. The birds just described that dash about and make sharp turns may be perfecting behavior that will help them later in getting away from danger or attacking a rival. Carrying bits of material in the air, dropping it and swooping after it as is done by some young falcons may be a preparation for retrieving small birds for food later on. This ultimate utility may have been instrumental in the development of play as a species characteristic. Some predatory birds go through the motions of attacking prey even when they are not hunting. A falcon will go through a flock of sandpipers without harming them, as though he were merely keeping in practice.

Care of Body Surface

Birds spend a lot of time in the care of their bodies. Some of us may seem to spend an inordinate amount of time with soap, lotions, creams and powders, but birds outdo us. Feathers require more care than skin, in any case, and a lot of time is spent oiling them. Birds pick at their oil glands, get a little oil on their bills and then anoint the feathers. Birds also bathe quite frequently, sometimes in water and sometimes in dust. Among other things, this helps to discourage insects, but afterward more oil is needed. One can notice interesting variations in bathing practices. Robins, for example, crowd into the bath together and have a wonderful time splashing around. A small flycatcher, however, bathes all by himself; he perches near the water, swoops down toward the bath, barely wets his underparts and zooms up to a branch, where he resumes preening.

In addition to preening, birds do a lot of scratching, presumably to dislodge insects. There are two ways to scratch the head: with the foot above the wing or under the wing. It was thought originally that species might be differentiated on this over-versus-under basis, but a specific study of this yielded essentially negative results. Birds were trapped and bits of paper stuck on their heads so that they would be sure to scratch, and then they were photographed in the process. Out of 207 individuals observed, 153 consistently scratched over the wing, 35 under and 19 both ways. It would seem that the actual pattern of scratching was not a species characteristic although the scratching itself was clearly an instinctive tendency [16].

Anting / A final type of behavior in the care of the body that has attracted considerable interest is "anting." This involves picking up ants with the bill and rubbing them on the feathers. A hand-raised orchard oriole, for example, was exposed to ants on 80 different days and went through the anting process on 67 of them. The average anting session was of 45 minutes duration [24]. At least 160 species of birds have been observed anting, and some 24 different kinds of ants have been used in the process.

The anting procedure may be active or passive. In the former, the bird holds the ant in the bill and anoints the feathers. In the latter, the birds stands or sits among the ants, fluffs its feathers and lets the ants crawl into its plumage, often assuming rather awkward postures in the process [3, p. 147]. Substances other than ants are sometimes used in the same manner. Grackles have been known to "ant" with mothballs. Other substances used include apple peels, mealworms, beer, vinegar, cigar butts, bits of onion, hair tonic and mustard.

The function of anting is not clear. It has been suggested that it is related to "feather maintenance" along with oiling and other preening. Other suggested reasons are for relieving itching, for a generally pleasant sensation or for control of parasites. There is a bit of empirical evidence on this matter of parasites. Some pipits were collected in Russia and all the mites on them collected in turn, counted and observed. Out of some 700 mites collected from pipits that were anting at the time, 90 were found to be dead and 163 died within 12 hours. When about the same number of mites was collected from nonanting pipits, only five died within 12 hours, suggesting that anting had something to do with mortality of the mites [12].

Nest and Family

We have noted the utility of some instincts in preserving the life of the individual; others function in preserving the species, that is, insuring successive generations. As noted, in the typical sex sequence the male selects his territory, defends it from other males and secures a mate. Together they build the nest, incubate the eggs, feed and care for the young, as part of the over-all pattern.

Nest / The location and construction of the nest follow the species pattern. Some species characteristically nest on the ground and some in trees, for example. It might be noted, however, that there is some adaptability in this, suggesting that evolution may be still in progress at the present time. There are places where ospreys nest on the ground on an island, but on the nearby mainland, where there are more terrestrial enemies, they nest in the treetops or other inaccessible places. Night herons nest on the ground in some western marshes although in other parts of the country they select tall trees in swamps [1, p. 77]. In addition to variations in the location of the nest, birds differ in the materials used and in the construction of the nest itself. Some nests have a roof; this is the case especially for species whose eggs are conspicuous. The grasshopper sparrow, for example, has white eggs that are readily seen, and it builds a roof over the nest to afford protection from any overhead predator.

It is usually assumed that the bird inherits the whole, full-blown tendency to build a nest in a particular pattern. This may not always be the case. Consider the weaverbird of Africa. In this species the male weaves a very elaborate nest. Some of these birds reared by hand in an aviary, when they reached the appropriate age, were given nesting material and observed carefully. It was obvious that they had a genetic tendency to collect flexible material and to weave after a fashion, but through practice in the process, they showed definite improvement. For instance, there was some improvement in the detail of just when to let go of a strip of grass that was being pulled through the part already woven. They also learned not to pull out a strip as soon as they had it in place [4]. The nesting of other species has not been observed in as much detail as this, and it is possible that the weaverbird is not typical. His nest is more complicated than those of most other species whose instinctive equipment may be adequate to take care of most types of nest. At any rate, the basic tendency is clearly instinctive.

In some cases the time of arrival at the breeding area seems to be genetic. Frequently, of course, the whole business of migration is much more complicated, involving such things as the development of the sex glands as well as meteorological factors. Purple martins, however, arrive at the breeding grounds some two months before they actually breed, and experts who have studied them claim that the time is "genetically determined" [11]. The early arrivals have better nesting sites available and have a certain reproductive advantage that may be passed on to their offspring, so there may be an evolution of "early" migrants.

Once young birds are hatched, the parents have to care for them until they are able to operate on their own. Sometimes the nestling, although very young indeed, helps out in the process. The young pied-billed grebe crawls up on its mother's back and is safer there than it would be moving around on an unstable floating nest in the swamp.

MISLEADING PREDATORS / A moot problem for parent birds is how to keep predators away from the young in the nest. One technique is to mislead the predator as to the location of the nest. A bobolink never flies directly to or from its nest but lands 10 or 15 feet away and walks over through the tall grass, then reverses the process when leaving. Thus any creature interested in finding the young bobolinks starts to look in the wrong place.

Another technique is to decoy the predator or instrument of potential danger away from the nest. The common killdeer puts on its broken-wing act for various animals and even for humans. It droops one wing as though it were broken and moves away from the nest in a rather irregular but conspicuous fashion. The predator usually follows the apparently injured bird, and when they are both a considerable distance from the nest, the broken wing heals suddenly and the parent bird flies away. One may uncritically interpret this broken-wing behavior as a very clever and intelligent procedure that the bird figures is a good way to distract a predator. It probably is nothing of the sort but merely an instinctive tendency that has some survival value. Individuals who had this particular mutation were more successful in raising their offspring to maturity, and the trait was passed along to the young. It is one of those cases where we have to be careful in interpreting a bit of behavior by a higher process when it can just as well be explained by a lower.

This decoy behavior is limited primarily to ground-nesting birds. Another type of decoying is practiced by the purple sandpiper in the north. If a man intrudes, for example, the sandpiper flies at him when he is 100 feet from the nest to get his attention. Then the bird fluffs its feathers till they resemble fur, droops and quivers its wing tips so that they look something like the hind legs of a rodent and then zigzags through the rocks and low plants, giving a thin call note that resembles that of a lemming. This behavior has been called a rodent run. It is especially useful in fooling the snowy owl, which is very fond of lemmings but does eat young purple sandpipers on occasion. The owl pursues the apparent lemming until it is led far away from the sandpiper's nest.

If the predator at the nest is not large, the parent bird may attack and often chase the enemy away. This behavior can be demonstrated by presenting a stuffed model of a species which ordinarily attacks the young, whereupon the parent attacks. Systematic experiments were made with willow warblers (European species), which are naturally hostile to cuckoos because the latter act as parasites and lay their eggs in the warbler's nest. A stuffed cuckoo on a long stick was lifted into a tree near where the male warbler had chosen his territory. He showed some aggressiveness during this stage, but after he had secured a mate, he made a more vigorous display toward the cuckoo but no actual attack. With eggs in the nest the warbler sometimes attacked the stuffed cuckoo although not invariably. After the hatching, with the young in the nest, he made violent attacks, continuing until the young were old enough to leave the nest and for some time thereafter. The tendency to attack the cuckoo thus became more pronounced as the nesting cycle advanced [19]. In Chapter IX we shall discuss some of these nesting problems in more detail.

Inflexibility

Many of the instinctive performances of birds seem remarkably efficient in serving their biological ends, but on some occasions the response to a situation may seem ridiculous by our standards. The birds have little resourcefulness when judgment is needed and may, for example, starve in the presence of unaccustomed food. Depending so much on their inherited and stereotyped behavior, birds are slow in adapting to new situations. Although this behavior has a high degree of evolutionary development and generally serves them effectively, when situations change, the instinctive tendency is often inflexible. We present a few instances of this.

Mistakes in recognition / The bird may fail to recognize the actual stimulus to which he normally reacts. One foggy dawn, a man was walking on a small sandy island off the New England coast, when a flock of brown creepers in migration came along; one landed on his trousers and walked up him in a somewhat spiral fashion. He shook himself and scared it off, but others came and did the same thing. Now the creeper's ordinary behavior is to land at the base of a small tree and move spirally upward, gleaning insects from the bark. The birds had blundered onto this little island where there were no trees, and as the only upright thing remotely resembling a tree trunk was the man standing there in the fog, they went through their instinctive repertoire. Another case of getting the wrong stimulus is the bird fighting to drive an "intruder" from its territory, mistaking its own reflection in a window or a car's hubcap for an intruder. There was a female redstart heading for her nest with a mouthful of food when by chance she alighted near a robin's nest. The young robins were clamoring so loudly for food that she gave it to them. Apparently her instinctive tendency was to put food in mouths, and it didn't matter much *which* mouths. Another case involved an oystercatcher which tried to incubate a huge artificial egg almost half as large as the bird itself [23, p. 164]. Thus, it was a rather inflexible type of behavior although it satisfied the instinctive urge.

A Muscovy duck has been noted to respond to the distress call of a mallard duckling and go over to "help." But if the mallard duckling was silent, the Muscovy responded to its color by killing it [23, p. 161]. Herring gulls sometimes, as noted earlier, drop a shellfish onto a large rock presumably in order to break it. This looks like considerable insight, but this assumption is invalidated when the bird sometimes drops the shellfish on mud or even on the water rather than on a rock. There is some evidence that crows are a little more consistent in dropping shellfish on rocks or on something hard such as a concrete road. Actually crows are considered somewhat more "intelligent" than many other species of birds [21, p. 51].

NEGLECTING PART OF SITUATION / Another instance of inflexibility is seen when the bird fails to take account of the whole situation. A killdeer built a nest on the gravel roof of a building. Ordinarily the nest is made in some pebbles on the ground and the young are presently able to scamper around in the nearby grass for food. The parents help direct them to food sources, all this happening before they are able to fly to any extent. The killdeer nest on the roof presented an impossible situation for the young, for there was no nearby field. The parents merely reacted to the gravel part of the situation and overlooked the roof part. Fortunately, some person knew enough to move the young to the ground, where the parents found them and all was well, despite the parent birds' lack of insight.

Other instances of shortsightedness in instinctive behavior involve reacting to a stimulus of the moment rather than the more appropriate objective. For example, certain boobies and some species of gull mutually attack each other's eggs or young. In one case a young gull was attacked by a boobie and gave its distress call. Thereupon, an adult gull came screaming to the rescue, but en route it saw an exposed boobie egg and stopped to eat that while its own young was being liquidated. It would seem that with a situation as serious as having one's own young killed, the gull would continue to the rescue objective rather than being distracted by food on the way.

Continuing unsuccessful activity / There are cases where the instinctive activity fails to work but the bird continues even though the behavior is obviously (to us) unsatisfactory. A California woodpecker that stores acorns in holes in trees may select a hole so deep that he cannot reach the acorns and so small that he cannot crawl in after them. On another occasion a woodpecker drilled a hole clear through a small tree. When he inserted acorns they dropped out on the other side. The bird persisted in this activity even though it was patently useless from the standpoint of storing acorns. Similarly, a jay dropped seeds through a hole in the roof of an empty cabin. It made an excellent storage area but the bird could not get inside the cabin. If a man were behaving thus we would say that he did not "think it through." With birds, at the least, instinctive behavior was inadequate.

The native tendency to enter an area where food is visible often leads the bird into a trap operated by a bird bander. If this is of the maze type described elsewhere the bird may enter again and again. He does not learn. One white-throated sparrow was trapped 40 times in 10 days. Finally he was taken several miles out of town and released on a migration route and did not return.

Similarly, the harlequin duck in Iceland normally swims upstream in swift rocky brooks and pokes its bill under stones after insect larvae but fails to adjust to lakes with still water, where larvae are abundant. In captivity it will not eat larvae in still water but must be provided with running water and some stones [22, p. 171].

These cases are understandable in the light of evolutionary theory. In earlier generations the tendency to go after visible food or to forage upstream under the rocks had survival value and thus evolved as an instinctive behavior. While an occasional bird might learn to do otherwise, this would not alter the genetic pattern. To make such a change it would have been necessary to have things arranged so that only those sparrows that stayed out of the trap survived or that the only surviving ducks were those that fed in still water.

One case may be mentioned where a specific environmental situation did have some influence on the instinctive pattern in several individuals. Young ducks from wild eggs, hatched and raised in an experimental aviary, when reaching maturity nested and incubated in normal fashion although remaining captive. Ducks raised in the wild and trapped when full grown and brought into the aviary did not select a suitable nesting site, some even laid eggs in the water. Thus the environment during the first year of the duck's life determined whether or not its instinctive breeding pattern would adapt itself to "civilization". [1, p. 131]. However, the eggs from the "civilized" pairs would not differ genetically from the other eggs. Breeding patterns would depend on whether the ducks hatched had spent their early lives in the wild or in the aviary.

Maturation

While instincts are inborn, they are not all manifest at birth. A bird is not strong enough to fly at the very outset, he cannot fight very much until he attains the proper development and some birds are blind at birth. However, the potentialities are there and come out on schedule. This tendency for the instinctive response to appear at the appropriate time subsequent to hatching is called maturation.

About the earliest time observed for an instinctive response to reach the maturation point was in the eggs of some grouse, whose young shortly before hatching may do some peeping. When the mother gave a call warning of a hawk overhead, the youngster inside the egg stopped peeping. The tendency to "hush" at the appropriate call from the parent is presumably instinctive in character and was sufficiently matured to be manifest even at this prenatal stage.

We may observe some maturation in connection with eating. All birds begin to ingest food quite early, but various species handle it differently. Chickens, ducks, turkeys, and quail for example peck at small seeds or grain soon after they are hatched, but at this stage robins and sparrows can merely extend the neck and open the mouth, whereupon the parent does the rest. The difference just mentioned highlights a common classification of birds on the basis of their behavior immediately after hatching. We call precocial those that are able almost immediately to run around and peck at food. We call altricial those species that are less competent at birth and have to be fed for a time by parents. At birth the precocial are at least covered with down, whereas the altricial are born practically naked. Both types go through the same stages of development but on a different schedule. One does much more development inside the egg.

The time at which various types of behavior appear is fairly constant in a given species. The song sparrow, for example, has been studied quite thoroughly. The young begin to scratch themselves fairly consistently when about seven days of age; they begin to bathe at 13 days [2, p. 188]. Similar schedules exist, doubtless, for other species.

The tendency to fly is native and develops at the appropriate time. Pigeons and birds of some other species if prevented by bandages from using their wings until they were full grown would then fly just as well as if nothing had happened [21, p. 39]. It is doubtful that the parents actually teach the youngster to fly. Some young birds, hawks for example, stand up in the nest and flap the wings for several days prior to the first takeoff. This is part of the maturation process.

Another of these responses that has a maturation period will be discussed later. At a certain critical period the tendency to follow a moving object develops and, the moving object usually present being the parent bird, the youngster thereafter follows birds of its own species. Occasionally, however, if a person walks by at that critical time, the bird will follow the person and continue to follow people the rest of its life. This tendency is called imprinting and may be considered, in a way, an instance of learning. But underlying it is the instinctive tendency to follow, which crops out at a particular stage.

Some instinctive behaviors are subject to modification through learning, such as the operation of picking up grain from the floor. A chick at the outset misses some bits at which it pecks, but this instinctive tendency develops greater accuracy as time goes on. Observers have counted hits and misses, determining that accuracy increased even during the first five days of life [5]. We shall discuss other instances of such modification in Chapter VI.

Thus we find birds quite well equipped with instinctive behaviors which account for a great deal of their activity. In the next chapter we shall consider one additional kind of instinctive behavior, migration, that is somewhat dramatic and merits discussion in its own right. Then we shall go on to the other principal type of behavior, learned behavior.

CHAPTER V

The Migration of Birds

Suddenly *we become aware that the* catbirds are no longer flying around the back yard. Or we notice only one robin pulling worms where until recently we had half a dozen working over the lawn. Then it dawns on us that migration is under way. Perhaps we are more alert to arrivals in the spring than to departures in the fall. The first springtime call of the red-winged blackbird across the road is dramatic. Even before that occurs we may see some white-throated sparrows for a few days on their way to breeding areas farther north. We may even observe the actual migration in progress. A V-shaped flock of geese flies over. Or at night we hear the chippering of small birds overhead on their nocturnal migration.

General Function

The utility of migratory behavior is obvious in many cases. The bird returns to its "birthplace" to raise its own young, presumably because the conditions that were suitable for one young generation will be suitable likewise for the next. On the other hand, if one lives in the far north on an exclusive diet of insects and these decrease in numbers with the advent of cool weather, there is only one thing to do. Flying out has the additional advantage of taking the bird away from prospective bad weather. Not that the bird figures it out in this manner—the instinctive urge to hit the ancestral flyway to the south simply comes along at about the right time. Not every bird leaves, however. The ruffed grouse manages to stay in the north the year round and dives into a snowbank for shelter. The brown ptarmigan likewise remains, turns white and lives by eating twigs after the insects are gone. Some birds faced with a food shortage do not migrate in the strict sense but forage farther and farther south by short stages. This is sometimes called an invasion (see below). In the tropics most birds never leave home, for life is easy in that climate. However, some species in Africa migrate, apparently to get away from the rainy season. The cardinals are the most widely observed permanent residents in the Temperate Zone, where in winter they manage to find adequate food and shelter. The average cardinal spends his entire life within a few miles of his birthplace, although an occasional bird goes a considerable distance—600 miles in one recorded case and 270 in another. The latter was recovered at a new more southerly location following five severe northeast snowstorms in the region where it was banded originally [2].

Actually only about 15 per cent of the world's species of birds migrate, although in the Temperate Zone the percentage is much larger. In central Ohio, for example, about 300 species are listed as having been seen and identified at some time. Of these only 23 are listed as permanent residents, which means that about 92 per cent are migrants [6]. At any rate, migration is a dramatic type of behavior and a challenge to the scientist who studies it.

Hibernation / An alternative method of coping with the rigors of winter is hibernation. Quite a number of animals do this, such as bears; but as far as is known only one bird has adopted this method. This is a Western species called the poor-will, which has been found in crevices in rocks in the dead of winter, its breathing and heartbeat almost imperceptible to an observer without instruments. Its body temperature when it hibernates is between 64 and 68 degrees, whereas normally it is around 106 [17]. This behavior evidently is a response to the lower temperature. This was demonstrated by subjecting a bird in a laboratory to a long period of low temperature, whereupon it exhibited the physiological tendencies just mentioned [16].

Invasion / A few species of birds come south some winters but not others, and certainly not on a regular basis, the invasion occurring in response to a food shortage as mentioned above. The most publicized has been the snowy owl, which is large and conspicuous. Normally it lives in the Arctic and feeds on lemmings (a type of rodent), but on occasion there is a shortage of lemmings, usually at four-year intervals. Some of the snowy owls then remain in the Arctic and starve; others go southward after food, a few flying out over the ocean and perishing there. A good many of them, however, reach southern Canada or the northern

United States to the delight of bird watchers. Incidentally, the shortage of lemmings may also cause an inadequate food supply for the snowy owls' nestlings, which die as a result.

Other invaders are smaller, less conspicuous and not so widely recognized as invaders. However, observers who keep records from year to year are well aware of some of these cases. The crossbills are a case in point. On occasion there will be a shortage of food in their northern habitat, such as a poor crop of cones on the evergreen trees, and then they appear in the central part of this country in larger numbers. It is the same story with the evening grosbeaks, which are conspicuous during certain winters at feeders that are well stocked with sunflower seeds. Invasion will occur when food must be searched for.

Another factor that occasionally produces invasions is overpopulation, observed with the Bohemian waxwings, for example, which breed in Finland but every ten years or so spread farther south in Europe. This has been attributed to an undue increase in population and all the pressures that go with overpopulation.

Schedule

Migration in the United States and Canada occurs in spring and fall, but there is the further question of just when it takes place. Most of us are more familiar with the spring aspect because we are alert to the first of this or that species. If we keep records from year to year, we may note some regularity in time of arrival. Even without a record we probably are aware that the red-winged blackbirds precede the warblers. Our records, of course, indicate when they arrive *here* in our area, not when they leave *there*. We shall discuss presently what starts them off from their wintering area to the south or their breeding grounds to the north.

There is a relationship in many cases between the distance they come and the time of arrival. Many of the early arrivals in northern states wintered in the southern states and along the Gulf Coast. Later we get some of the warblers and vireos from South America, who winter on the slopes of the Andes and in the pampas of Brazil [1, p. 139].

Even though a species is uniformly early or late in arriving, there is considerable variation of the exact date from year to year.

For example, in central Ohio the black-and-white warbler is first seen about April 21, on the average, but one year the earliest arrival was April 5. With some species the sexes differ in their time of arrival, the male red-winged blackbirds preceding the females by two weeks or so, although a few ornithologists believe that many females arrive about as early as the males but keep out of sight.

For the birds that spend the summer with us we have satisfactory records of times of arrival and departure. But it is more difficult to determine the schedules of migrants that are passing through in either direction. A bird may be with us merely overnight or may linger several days. Unless we can identify the individual bird interpretation is difficult. That is one reason for numerous projects involving trapping and banding (and often rebanding) birds along the spring and fall flyways. These projects provide much information as to schedules of migrants passing through our area.

Some migration schedules reflect local weather conditions. We are not concerned at the moment with the weather as a trigger that starts them off from their original location but rather with weather influences en route. Hawks are a conspicuous example. A lot of their progress over long distances is made by gliding rather than by flapping the wings continuously. If a hawk can find a thermal (a column of rising air), it is possible for him to glide in big circles with little effort to reach a considerable height. Then he makes a long glide along the "ridge" in the desired direction. When he nears the ground again, hopefully he can pick up another thermal. This behavior can be quite spectacular at the right place and time when hundreds of hawks may participate simultaneously. While hawk migration occurs at certain approximate dates, a closer prediction can be made on the basis of weather that produces these thermals as well as from favorable or unfavorable wind direction.

There are other cases where migration seems to follow a particular temperature condition. On occasion large numbers of migrating robins and Canada geese have been found strung out across the country on a line where the temperature was just above 35 degrees. As this temperature line (isotherm) moved northward the birds tended to go along with it [9, p. 238], suggesting that for these particular birds there was no great rush, and they lingered as long as there were favorable temperature conditions. Other species such as the warblers seem more precise about the matter and more motivated toward their real objective so that they keep going with less regard for local temperature.

Terminal Points

Migration is essentially traveling from the breeding grounds, which may be synonymous with summer residence, to the winter quarters and vice versa. The individual bird takes his first trip from the breeding grounds to the wintering area when only a few months old. Summer and winter areas often have similar conditions with reference to general geography, trees or grass, dryness or wetness and food supply, which is one reason some migrants will go fantastically long distances in order to find the right place. These terminal points were worked out in the course of evolution and now are pretty much part of the instinctive migratory pattern for a given species.

More information is available about breeding grounds than about winter quarters because we can often see the nests. The birds stick fairly close to the nesting area at least during the breeding season and probably do not move too far away for the rest of the summer provided the food holds out. In winter quarters they are more scattered, and there are few obvious "hangouts."

The tendency is quite general to return in spring to the approximate nesting area of the preceding year. In numerous instances birds banded at the breeding grounds are captured the next year in the same general area [8, p. 42]. Around home we sometimes see the same nest occupied a second year, but we cannot be sure that it is the same bird unless he has been marked in some fashion. But if a banded bird is caught in the same trap in the same yard a year later, the presumption is that he is nesting in the same vicinity. There was an authenticated case of a sapsucker that returned to the same hole that he had used for a nest the year previous while all the other sapsuckers in the vicinity were drilling new holes. The sad story was that he could not interest a female in sharing the old hole. It is tempting to get anthropomorphic about this [18].

Species that nest in colonies have been observed returning to the same colony. An extensive 12-year study was made of common terns at Cape Cod with appropriate techniques for identifying individual birds in several colonies. It was found that 75 per cent returned to the same colony where they had been hatched, and in the most stable colonies the figure was 83 per cent. After the first nesting, the terns tended to return the next year and actually establish themselves very close to their first nest. Records were kept of the exact location, and the distances of the new sites from the old were measured. Some 20 per cent of the birds came within five feet of the original site and 80 per cent within 25 feet [3]. The Laysan albatross nesting on Midway Island does even better. It was found that the greatest deviation in location of the second nest from the first was 13 inches [19].

There are instances where difficulty is experienced in returning to the birthplace to nest. A typical case, confirmed by banding, involved a female mallard duck hatched in Ontario and a male hatched in Saskatchewan. They went south for their first winter and "met" in Louisiana. Many birds pair off prior to migration north, and these two did. The problem was to return to the birthplace, but here there were two birthplaces involved. In this case they went to Ontario, where the female had originated. We can merely speculate as to the psychological mechanisms involved. Perhaps the female took off for Ontario and the male simply went along. The tendency to stay with the female was greater than the tendency to return to his ancestral breeding area.

Whether or not the individual always returns to the same winter area we cannot say. A wintering area may not be as specific as a breeding colony. However, there are isolated instances noted of return to the same area winter after winter. Many juncos spend the winter someplace in the Temperate Zone and sometimes the same junco is trapped and identified in the same yard several winters in succession. The writer had several that returned to his trap after two or three years and one after four years. Similarly, three tree sparrows marked with colored bands for identification returned to the same feeder the next year. They also came on the second and third years to the same spot, and one of them made it on the fourth year [1, p. 136].

In the tropics many of these rules do not operate. Some birds nest in the Sahara and merely go farther north for the summer to the Barbary Coast. This is scarcely winter quarters in our sense of the term; it might be better to call it a rest area. Still farther south the situation may be somewhat as it is in the north except displaced by six months. Some birds that breed in the south end of South America come north in April to "winter" in Brazil. Similar situations in Africa are not as pronounced because there is not as much variation in the climate. (Southern Hemisphere seasons are, of course, the opposite of those in the Northern Hemisphere.)

Routes

When birds leave the breeding grounds, they do not start off in all directions but follow a fairly definite route. However, it is nothing like our driving on a highway a few feet wide. Birds are not limited by pavement, trees, fences or even small lakes, and they do not go single file but may proceed on a front several miles wide.

General flyways / There are some general flyways or routes on which there is considerable concentration of migrants. For example, the Mississippi River can be seen for an appreciable distance from each side of the river by birds from the air.

It is common practice among ornithologists to designate four major flyways in the United States: the Atlantic, the Mississippi, the Central and the Pacific. The Atlantic Flyway involves primarily the states that have at least some Atlantic coastline. The Mississippi Flyway, as the name implies, has the river down the center of it, with the states on each side involved to some extent. The Central Flyway lies between Montana and the Dakotas and extends about straight south from there, again taking in some states on each side of that central line. The Pacific Flyway involves the coastline and a tier of states inland from it. The Federal Fish and Wildlife Service has adopted these flyways for the coding of their data about bird banding and migration; for example, noting in which of the four flyways the bird was banded or recovered for classification purposes. Some of the concentration of migrants noted may be due to convenience and to landmarks. It is easy to follow a coastline or a big river without getting lost, but birds sometimes follow smaller rivers or are influenced by the larger lakes so that they veer away from the flyway. In North America there are no major obstacles along the north-south flyways. In Europe and Asia there are more mountains to interfere, while the Mediterranean Sea is an appreciable obstacle. Many migrants go east in order to bypass the Mediterranean and then bear west again before heading south. Nor does the flyway mean that *all* birds of a given species follow a particular one of the four flyways. They may start from widely different points if the breeding grounds happen to be strung out across the country. Even though they start from the same point, they do not always take the handiest flyway but for some reason of their own may move over to one of the others.

It is interesting to note the migration routes for some species that do not follow the standard flyway. The Arctic tern, for example, breeds in western Greenland and northeast Canada. In migration it swings to the coast of Europe and down the coast of Africa. While some continue down the African coast to the end and then across the water to their ultimate destination near Antarctica, others cross from the bulge of Africa to the bulge of South America and then go down the South American coast to their destination.

Golden plovers follow a different route going north from that used when flying south. After breeding in northern Canada, they take off through Labrador, then cross the ocean to the north coast of South America and thence to the Argentine. On the return trip, they come up through Central America and then hit the Mississippi Flyway to the north. Another group of golden plovers breeds in Alaska and migrates directly to the Hawaiian Islands for the winter.

The smaller birds migrate likewise but not in quite as dramatic a fashion. The scarlet tanager breeds in the northern and northeastern United States in an area perhaps 2000 miles wide, but the migrants funnel into a 600-mile front by the time they reach the Gulf of Mexico. They cross the Gulf to Central America on a front about 100 miles wide and eventually reach Peru and Bolivia. Most of the warblers go to South America, but the Kirtland warbler is unique. Known to breed only in a limited area in central Michigan, it winters in the Bahamas. It never seems to miss either destination because the birds are never found except in those two places. Migration ordinarily implies "flying someplace." Actually some penguins do a little migration merely by swimming, although they do not migrate very far.

There are interesting cases where a species has expanded its range through a long course of years into a new territory, after which the migrating birds seem to retrace the historical expansion path. The pectoral sandpipers were originally limited to Arctic North America, then they spread into north and central Siberia. Now the Siberian pectorals migrate via Alaska to the central Arctic and then down the Central or Mississippi Flyway to Central America and Argentina [39, p. 456].

Similarly the wheatear, which spread from Europe to Greenland and then to Labrador, now migrates via Greenland to Europe and down the coast to Africa. This throwback to the ancestral route is interesting and probably genetic. There is little indication that migrating birds teach the young ones which route to follow. More likely the use of that route has some survival value.

Occasional deviations from the regular route are found. We have mentioned going around the Mediterranean, but sometimes smaller bodies of water may divert migrants to some extent. When hawks reach the shore of Lake Ontario and cannot see across, they head eastward along the shore to bypass the Lake. Another factor is the absence of thermals or updrafts over the lake—and hawks like to ride thermals rather than fly. Lake Erie, on the other hand, has facilities for island hopping by the migrants. There is also a tendency to follow valleys and streams, which to some extent provide landmarks. Birds will also deviate from a standard route in the search for food if they are not making a nonstop flight. If they drop down for food and find none, they may explore some distance from the flyway.

One other route for migration may be mentioned: upward. The juncos in the Great Smoky Mountains of Tennessee merely go up or down the mountain 4000 feet to get warmer or cooler climates or more favorable conditions for whatever they want to do at that particular season. This 4000 feet up is about the equivalent of going 1200 miles north with reference to the regional ecology of trees, shrubs, food and the like. Some chickadees may migrate 8000 feet up or down a mountain.

Distance

Implicit in the preceding discussion of terminal points and routes is the fact that birds sometimes migrate a considerable distance, but the Arctic tern takes the prize. Some of them are known to start 450 miles from the North Pole and go 11,000 miles to their southern destination—a round trip of 22,000 miles every year. However, some nest on Cape Cod and cut the distance considerably. The golden plover migrating from Labrador to its wintering grounds in South America flies 2400 miles each way, and we have mentioned another golden-plover trip from Alaska to Hawaii of 2000 miles. An albatross banded in Australia turned up in the Falkland Islands, 7000 miles away.

Some of the smaller birds do pretty well, also. The blackpoll warbler nests around Hudson Bay and winters in Venezuela or even farther south, traveling in the year some 10,000 miles. Even the little hummingbird makes a 500-mile nonstop flight over the Gulf of Mexico, then after an appropriate rest, continues some distance beyond. A shearwater was taken from its nest in Wales, transported to Boston and released. Twelve days later it was back at the nest 3200 miles away. This was not actual migration, but it was an appreciable distance.

One might wonder whether or not these long flights are really necessary. The probable answer, as mentioned earlier, is that birds tend to winter in a place that is similar to the breeding area with reference to food, vegetation and general geography. It has been suggested that on these long flights they may keep on because they "enjoy" flying [1, p. 136]. While it is conceivable that a bird might be keyed up and unnecessarily keep going, it is difficult to see how this tendency would become fixed in the species, because its survival value is not clear.

Speed

Some migrants fly quite rapidly. There are some data available where a bird was banded in one place and recovered rather soon in some other place at a known distance. Yellowlegs banded on Cape Cod appeared in Martinique six days later and 1900 miles distant, averaging about 316 miles per day. Similarly, one mallard duck flew 510 miles in two days, another, 550 miles, which would average 275 per day. Chimney swifts are known to have moved 600 miles in four days. We cannot reduce these figures to miles-per-hour because there is no information as to the hours spent in flight per day [38, p. 204].

There are some indications that birds fly faster on migration than they do ordinarily. Starlings fly between 23 and 32 miles per hour but when migrating go 46. Corresponding figures for barn swallows are 29–32 m.p.h. ordinarily and 34–37 when migrating. It is possible that a bird has a "comfortable" speed of flight just as the average person normally walks at about a certain rate. But the matter is flexible, and deviations from the comfortable rate are frequent [9, p. 217]. As to the basic cause of the more rapid flight of migrants, we cannot be certain. It is possible that the mere presence of other fliers stimulates the bird to a little more vigorous activity because of social facilitation. On the other hand, there may be some drive connected with migration itself that stimulates the birds to greater effort. The endocrines that help initiate the migration itself may push the bird along toward his objective at greater than usual speed. Whatever the cause, the birds obviously have some "reserve" and, if it becomes necessary, they can put on additional speed. The more rapid migratory flight may have some minor advantage such as shorter exposure to whatever hazards are met en route. It also leaves more time for foraging at the end of the daily flight.

Not all migrating birds are in such a hurry. We mentioned elsewhere that robins coming up from the Gulf Coast averaged 13 miles a day. Obviously they were not flying all day long and may even have stopped a day or two en route.

The ordinary speed of flight for various birds has been determined by several different techniques such as following them by car or by airplane or tracking them by radar. Small land birds seem to do about 20 to 30 miles per hour, ducks 40 to 55 and some of the shorebirds 40 to 60. Starlings in ordinary flight have been clocked at between 23 and 32 miles per hour and hummingbirds from 45 to 60. Among the more rapid birds, the red-breasted merganser was tracked at 100 miles per hour for a short burst of speed, while some of the falcons in a power dive after prey reach 150 momentarily. As suggested above, some of the figures may be raised a bit during migration.

There are also other situations where a bird will draw on his reserve and put on a burst of speed—when chased by a predator, for example, there is maximum motivation and the accelerator "goes down to the floorboard." The predator in turn does likewise.

Night Versus Day

Some birds migrate at night, some by day and some do both. One frequently sees a flock of geese or ducks flying over in the appropriate direction. On the other hand, one often hears a lot of chippering sounds overhead at night.

In a general way, it seems that the day migrants are strong flyers, normally ranging over fairly wide areas. They include geese, ducks, herons, swallows and chimney swifts. On the other hand, the weak-flying, secretive or shy birds fly more at night. They include sparrows, warblers, vireos, wrens, tanagers, cuckoos and rails. But geese, ducks and many shorebirds fly at night also. One sees geese in a V-shaped formation during the daytime and also hears their honk overhead at night [8, p. 36].

There are some possible advantages to night migration, at least for the species that follow this system. It helps birds to avoid predators to which many of these weak flyers are vulnerable. On a long hop, especially, it is advantageous to end the trip in the early daylight so that the bird can forage for food. If he arrives toward dark, food is more of a problem.

The nocturnal migrants do not necessarily fly all night, for some radar studies over Switzerland showed that the biggest flights came between 10 P.M. and 1 A.M. The number of migrants picked up on the radar screen began to decrease after midnight and had practically disappeared by 4 A.M. Just what the birds did from then until daylight was not determined [9, p. 255].

Altitude

Most migration takes place at altitudes of less than a mile. At Cape Cod radar indicated that during the three or four hours after sunset the most frequent height was 1525 feet above sea level. Some 90 per cent of the birds spotted were below 5000 feet and 99 per cent below 10,000 feet. A few, however, did migrate at lower than 600 feet. The small perching birds tended to fly somewhat higher than the others, but the radar picked up echoes at 20,000 feet that probably were shorebirds either starting or ending a long sea crossing. These results in general were a bit lower than some obtained by radar in England, where migrants were between 1500 and 6000 feet and occasionally were at 10,000 feet [30].

Some data on birds seen from an airplane at a known altitude include strong-flying shorebirds at 5000 to 6000 feet, ducks at 7500 and geese at 9000. This was over areas where there was little high ground in the underlying terrain. In the high mountains it may be somewhat different. Birds have been found pretty well up in the Himalayas and the Andes. In fact, some geese crossing the Himalayas in India were reported at 29,500 feet [10].

There are also a few cases on record where birds have been hit by an airplane at some high altitudes. These reports include an evening grosbeak at 12,500 feet, a gold-crowned sparrow at 10,000 and a mallard duck at 21,000. These are extreme cases, however, and we do not know why the bird was so far off its course in a vertical direction.

A tendency has been observed for land birds to fly higher when over the water. Ordinarily they notice landmarks such as trees, rivers or small lakes. If necessary they can fly higher and pick up the more distant landmarks, and perhaps they make such an effort when over the ocean where there are no landmarks. Conceivably the tendency to fly high over unfamiliar territory could have some survival value.

Social Aspects

Migration often takes place in flocks and looks like a social project. The birds call back and forth during flight, but whether this is actual "conversation" or an automatic device to keep the flock intact is problematical. It could be that the birds make similar sounds when migrating alone. Singing during ordinary flight is not unusual. A goldfinch all by himself has a very characteristic flight song.

Migration appears to be something more than a lot of birds that happen to be going in the same direction at the same time. Even when there is no definite formation, the edges of the group are fairly well defined and one can say that the flight pattern is so many feet wide. The formation is more conspicuous when the flock takes on some definite shape such as the V followed by some geese or a compact oval we often find with ducks.

Some species gather before migration and seem to be preparing for the social aspects of the trip. Swallows become conspicuous on the wires as the season approaches. Blackbirds sometimes have a roost at night a short time prior to the actual takeoff. Some ducks have been observed to gather on cloudy days, preparing, as it were, for prompt departure when the weather broke. As noted elsewhere, birds often have difficulty in navigating on a long flight in cloudy weather, when they cannot see the sun or stars—hence the delay. The migration urge gets them together but they hold back until conditions are meterologically favorable [29]. Even some species, like the stork in Europe, that are ordinarily quite solitary get together for migration purposes and then disperse when they have reached the destination. Short-eared owls do the same thing.

This togetherness at migration time is often quite in contrast to behavior at the breeding season, when individual birds are aggressively defending their territory and certainly do not want other birds around except the mate that is sharing the territory. But at the end of the nesting season there is no need to keep other birds away, so there is no aggressive resistance to going along with others on a migratory flight.

There may be some advantages in group migration. For one thing, if the species is subject to predators, the flock is less apt to be vulnerable than is an individual bird. A predator seldom dives right into the middle of a flock to seize a bird—he is more inclined to work along the edges and pick off stragglers, so the grouping has a survival aspect. There is also a possibility that flying in the wake of the bird ahead means reduction of air resistance and saves some energy. Pelicans are supposed to utilize this principle quite consistently. We have mentioned already the tendency to fly somewhat more rapidly in a migrating flock and its possible advantages.

Another minor advantage accrues to the shorebirds that migrate in groups over long distances. The males and females do part of their courting en route. This may save a little time in sorting out when they reach their final destination and they can begin the business of building nests with less delay. Perhaps this has some biological advantage.

Techniques of Studying Migration

Banding / Implicit in the foregoing discussion is the fact that information about migration has been obtained by a variety of methods. It might be well at this point to review these briefly and then proceed to some of the more experimental work. Bird banding has contributed a lot of information about migration. Wild birds are captured by some type of trap or caught in a large net stretched across a flyway, or perhaps the young are taken from the nest and then banded by having a small light aluminum band containing a serial number clamped around the leg. This band is so small that it does no harm to the bird and does not handicap him at all; he is released immediately. The size of the band used depends on the leg size. Cooperators properly licensed all over the country are banding birds, and the results are all sent in to the research center of the Wildlife Service at Patuxent, Maryland, which issues the bands as well as takes care of the licensing. The data are put on IBM cards, making it possible to look up any particular band and find out on what bird it was put, when and where. So if a bird is shot, found dead or trapped again by some bander, the number can be sent to headquarters and the bird traced. If a robin is banded in Ohio and recovered in Florida, we know at least two places he visited during his life and we have some notion as to how far he migrated; also, we may determine how long he lived.

The first case of bird banding on record was in 1710 when a bird banded in Turkey was found in Germany. Audubon banded some phoebes in this country in 1803. In the United States and Canada up to now, some eleven million bands have been applied to birds, and upwards of half a million are added yearly. In 1963 45,600 bands were recovered. For small birds perhaps 1 per cent of those banded are recovered, while with the larger, more conspicuous birds the figure may be 3 or 4 per cent. We get still higher proportions among some of the game birds when hunters turn in the bands on the birds they have shot. For the most part, the bands are taken on dead or trapped birds. In a few instances bands have been found in owl pellets. Owls eat their prey, bones and all, later disgorging a pellet containing the bones and other indigestible material, such as animal hair or bird feathers. A great horned owl pellet contained a band that had been placed on a coot four months before he was eaten. Two chickadee bands were found in the pellet of a screech owl and a band from a young bluejay appeared in a long-eared-owl pellet.

Radar / A few ornithologists have access to radar equipment and have used this for observing migration. The radar beam sweeps the sky just as is done in looking for airplanes. On the screen appear reflections from individual birds or flocks of birds. The screen usually is photographed periodically and the photographs analyzed. It is possible to check the speed of the flock by noticing the distance between the dots on successive pictures taken with a finite lapse of time. The interpretation of these pictures is somewhat technical and beyond the scope of the present discussion. Radar is not very effective for birds flying over 6400 feet above the level of the transmitter [12].

Moon watching / If one trains a small telescope on the full moon during the migration season, he often can see birds fly across the face of the moon. Some of the smaller ones look like mere dots, but some of the larger ones actually look like birds. One can note a surprising number of migrants in this fashion, although it is difficult to tell how far away the bird actually is. But it has been demonstrated that with a 20-power telescope one can see a warbler about a mile distant as a recognizable spot. Usually this technique involves two people working as a team, one with his eye at the telescope and the other writing down what the first one says. The observer counts the birds and indicates the direction in which they cross the moon, for example, "10 o'clock to 4 o'clock."

Other methods / Another type of nocturnal observation deals with the calls given by the birds as they fly over. One who can recognize the call notes of different species may get some notion as to the number of birds of each species flying over in a given length of time. Possibly a better approach is to record the sounds on tape and then analyze them at leisure.

COLLISION WITH OBSTACLES / Birds migrating at night encounter many hazards in the form of tall obstacles. They fly into tall buildings or monuments and frequently encounter radio or television towers, with which contact is usually fatal, and a considerable number of birds are found in the morning at the foot of such towers. Taking a census of the birds killed provides a fair sample of the migrants passing through that particular area.

One study might be mentioned as an example of an indefatigable observer. At a television tower in Florida, the observer kept the grass closely cut in the surrounding area so that the birds could be found. He reduced predation by catching great horned owls in the area and deporting them a considerable distance away. He patrolled the area every morning from October, 1955, until June, 1961. Of course, between the main migration periods there would not be very many casualties, but he nevertheless checked the area daily. This shows the dedication of at least one ornithologist [37].

CAPTURED AND RELEASED BIRDS / Quite a few special studies have been made with birds that were captured by traps or nets, those taken from the nest and even with resident birds in an aviary. These are banded or otherwise marked and released at various distances from "home" and notes made of how many return and how rapidly they reappear. Birds that have been captured are released and followed with binoculars to see the direction of their initial flight. Small battery lights may be placed on the legs of birds released at night so that they can be followed for some distance. Still further studies have been made by following the released birds in airplanes to get a notion of their direction of flight especially in the early stages after being released in strange territory. Better still, a light radio transmitter may be attached to the bird and the plane equipped with a receiver tuned to the transmitter frequency. Then it is not necessary even to see the bird. In fact, one thrush was followed thus all night.

Migratory restlessness / Another method for studying migration, described in Chapter III, utilizes the fact that captive birds fly around the cage much more often as the migration season approaches. Their activity (and its direction) is recorded electronically.

Stimuli for Migration

Migration schedules show some regularity. Birds of a species do not leave at random. The stimuli or triggers that set them off seem to be of two general kinds: internal factors such as glands and external factors such as weather. The internal stimuli get the bird ready for migration, although the final takeoff may vary several days one way or the other according to meteorological conditions.

Fat deposits / One observable change as migration approaches is the increased amount of fat in the bird's body. Migration involves a large expenditure of energy, and fat is the standard "fuel" for birds. It is an efficient fuel, a given weight of fat producing about two and one half times as many calories of energy as does the same weight of sugar products. The bird takes on this fuel by eating. The golden plover, for example, fills up on bayberries before starting his 2,400-mile nonstop flight south, and warblers eat more insects than usual for several days before attempting the Gulf of Mexico. Postmortem examinations have shown this increase of fat reserve prior to migration in many species, and examinations after flight show that the weight then is often below normal. The golden plover just mentioned loses two ounces on the trip, which is quite a lot for a shorebird. Again, migrants blown way off their course and presumably traveling much farther than they would normally are found to weigh 20 to 30 per cent less than they should.

An interesting metabolic study was made with a hummingbird. It was put in an appropriate chamber where it hovered for about a minute, its metabolism being recorded by appropriate instruments during that period. The results were translated into terms of the amount of fat used in a given length of time. If straight flying were considered about as strenuous as hovering, it worked out that with two grams of fat as fuel the hummingbird at 250 miles an hour could do 650 miles, which would be enough to cross the Gulf [22].

While fat accumulation consistently precedes migration, it is not necessarily the trigger for it. In fact, one study showed that fat was not the actual cause. Small sparrowlike birds (bramblings) in England were kept confined during what would be the premigratory period, and the hours for feeding and the quantity of food were controlled so that they could not accumulate any fat. Nevertheless at the appropriate time they did develop the typical migratory restlessness, indicating that there was something more basic than the fat. It could be that the same stimulus that starts birds eating and accumulating fat also triggers the migration [23].

GLANDS / In Chapter III we discussed the development of the sex glands (gonads) and the pituitary as possible stimuli for migration and also noted how seasonal changes in the relative amounts of light and darkness influenced the development of the glands, which in turn influenced the migration. It appears that the basic drive is glandular, touching off the tendency to eat and accumulate fat, to get restless and all the rest of the complicated migratory pattern which ensues.

EXTERNAL STIMULI / When the internal stimuli indicate that migration time has arrived, local conditions may make a difference of a few days one way or the other. Generally some aspect of the weather touches off the actual departure. In spring some species have been observed to start north when there are south winds, a rising temperature and a falling barometer. The warm winds are caused by a low-pressure area moving from southwest to northeast, and the number of birds that take off is almost proportional to the lowering of the barometer and the extent of the depression [31]. Conversely, if birds encounter a cold front, the migration usually stops immediately or at least within 24 hours. There are some cases where birds migrate into a sudden cold front and turn around to go in the other direction for a time. It has also been observed that overcast may delay migration somewhat, presumably because of difficulty in navigation.

The autumn migration seems more dependent on these external

stimuli because the internal are not as active. Nesting is over. Cold may be enough to set them off; likewise, hunger, if food is getting scarce. Radar studies in Illinois showed that the autumn migration of perching birds coincided with a change in the wind from south to north. Cold fronts also were involved, but if the winds changed in the day and the front did not come along until night, the birds reacted to the wind. In some cases a tail wind was found to be helpful in stimulating migration [14]. Similarly, shorebirds in the same region tended to leave when there was a clockwise wind shift to the north [7].

Some birds apparently do not need the external stimulus. Swifts leave on almost the same date every year. Cuckoos have been found to leave for the south when there was no apparent change in the season and when insect food was still abundant. For them it was simply "the time."

We even find cases where a species migrates in two waves, which might be called "weather migrants" and "instinctive migrants." The former come along early in spring, the others somewhat later. In Ohio the song sparrow does this. The early wave is mostly males of the local breeding population that seem to come when the weather is favorable. The later wave is not so clearly related to the weather and seems to depend more on the internal drives.

HOMING

WE have seen that birds do a lot of traveling. The final question is how they reach the correct destination. In moving around the local area or neighborhood, they do much as we do, observing familiar landmarks—the big tree above the nest or the fence beside the yard in which their territory lies. With the longer trips we cannot be so sure. Sometimes it is just a matter of going home, except flying a much greater distance, but migrating from the Arctic to the Antarctic poses a real problem of finding the way.

We may get some knowledge of the cues used in migration by considering how homing birds find their way. Birds have been taken various distances from the nest or home loft to see if they would return and how soon [9, p. 322]. The maximum distance for successful homing in a few cases was song sparrow, 35 miles;

grackle, 62; cowbird, 300; red-wing, 210; starling, 440; and purple martin, 234. We mentioned already the shearwaters that homed from Boston to Wales—some 3,200 mlies.

LANDMARKS / More important than distance in the present connection is *how* they do it. One possibility is evident in the following incident. Cliff swallows taken 25 miles out to sea were unsuccessful in returning to their nests although they returned 25 miles over land fairly well [24]. Landmarks made the difference, and they may be involved more than we suspect in homing flights of considerable distance. It is possible that birds forage over a much larger area than we realize and learn some fairly distant landmarks.

The importance of topographic cues was shown in the following study. When pigeons raised in open aviaries were taken 90 miles away, 15 to 20 per cent of them made it home again. However, if they were raised with a barrier around the aviary that obscured the view for 3 degrees above the horizon, they were not successful in homing from a distance. Evidently they needed to become familiar with topographic features along the horizon from their aviary so as to use those features later in homing [20]. In a similar study where the aviary was placed in a depression that cut off the view of the horizon, much the same results were obtained.

WATCHING TAKEOFF / We may get some pertinent information by observing with binoculars the early stages of flight from the release point. Cliff swallows, released at some distance from familiar territory, made a random radial search or flew in spirals at the outset. Presumably some of them then picked up familiar landmarks. Shearwaters, on the other hand, showed initial orientation directly toward the home base. Pintail ducks show both tendencies. Sometimes they head in the correct direction at the outset and sometimes they take circuitous routes. Mallard ducks, with flashlights attached to their legs to facilitate night observing, when released 11 miles from home headed immediately in the correct direction.

Gannets from Bonaventure Island, carried inland and released, then followed by an airplane, flew very irregular paths and were obviously exploring. However, carrier pigeons observed from a plane went in the correct direction at the outset. Obviously, there is no consistent tendency. In some cases the bird goes directly toward home and in others has to explore. There is even a suggestion that some birds use both systems. Pigeons released at various distances from the home loft seemed to orient pretty well at less than 12 miles or more than 75 miles, but in between their activity was more random. Perhaps when close they handled the situation by landmarks and when at a considerable distance they navigated by the stars or sun; in betweeen, they tried to do both and got confused [26].

We still do not know just what cues the birds use. In the next section we shall discuss celestial navigation. It has been suggested that when we take them to the point of release, they somehow remember the path they followed—how many turns, about how far in each direction—and then merely follow the course in reverse. But many times the bird is in some enclosed container so that he cannot see the landscape as he goes along. If it were a question of remembering the sensations of moving, that has been pretty well ruled out. This was tested by carrying the birds on a train and putting the cage on a turntable that revolved continuously, in one case revolving 5000 times during a trip of 93 miles, but still the birds returned.

It has been found also that birds home less effectively on a cloudy day or a foggy night, which suggests that they receive cues from the sky. Also it has been noted that nonmigratory species have poorer homing ability than migratory species. The latter might conceivably be more alert to celestial cues.

One study of displaced birds deserves mention in more detail. This was not exactly homing in the sense just discussed but involved coming back to the same place to winter. Some 411 white-crowned and golden-crowned sparrows, wintering near San Jose, California, were taken by plane to Baton Rouge, Louisiana, and then released there. The following winter—not the winter when released—26 came back to San Jose. Then 660 birds were taken from San Jose to Laurel, Maryland, and 15 returned to San Jose the following winter. Six birds made *both* trips successfully. The hypothesis suggested is that the displaced birds somehow found their way to their breeding grounds in Alaska and then followed their normal migration route to San Jose the following winter. It is to be noted that none of them came back directly from the displaced location the same winter they were taken away. The experiment demonstrated ability to get home from a geographical area beyond their experience. If they did it via Alaska, there is still the question of how they found Alaska from the new location. We shall discuss some of these problems in the next section [27].

Navigation

We have seen that when homing from considerable distances some birds explore in various directions until they hit some familiar landmarks while others start right off correctly, as if they sensed the direction of home. Migration of hundreds of miles, however, surely requires more than landmarks.

Ancestral compass direction / When a bird starts in a specific direction from the point of experimental release or from the breeding grounds or from the winter quarters, one of his observed tendencies is to go in the same compass direction that his ancestors used for migrating. If birds of his species have been going to a destination that is exactly southwest from the starting point, all he has to do is go southwest until he reaches the right place. This is presumably what happened in some of the instances cited earlier like the golden plover that hops from Labrador to South America. It will be recalled also that in studies of migratory restlessness, even birds without experience spent most of their time on the appropriate sector of the cage wall, *i.e.*, in the correct compass direction.

When birds were displaced well to the side of their normal migration route, they took off in a direction parallel to it. In some cases the birds captured were in the course of migration on a southwesterly course; moved a considerable distance to one side, they proceeded again on a southwesterly course, which now would bring them to the wrong destination. Young crows in eastern Germany were banded and some of them recovered a little later in their breeding grounds east of the Baltic, to reach which involved a northeasterly flight. Some other young crows from the same part of eastern Germany were taken 465 miles to the west and released in southern Denmark; presently they appeared in a location directly northeast of where they were released. Evidently they took off in the ancestral direction and when they had traveled about the normal distance they settled down [28]. Similarly, starlings in the autumn were released well to one side of their normal line of flight and recoveries analyzed. Those who had migrated to their winter quarters before made it somehow, while juveniles with no experience of that goal went parallel to the direction normally followed by that species and thus reached the wrong winter quarters. However, they did ultimately get back to their original summer region. How the adults corrected for the displacement is not clear.

Imitation / When young birds that have never migrated before start off with mature birds, obviously they can receive some guidance. Even if they do have a genetic direction tendency, they may not need it. Some of the displacement experiments bring out this fact. Mallard duck eggs from England (where the species is nonmigratory) were taken and hatched in Finland. The ducks migrated southeast with the native ducks. Evidently there was enough tendency to go with the flock to offset any genetic tendency to stay put, like their English ancestors.

A more critical situation occurs when young birds are released *after* the older ones have departed. In that case the genetic tendency has an unequivocal opportunity to operate. Young crows which were raised in Alberta were not released until after all the adults had gone south and the ground was covered with snow. The youngsters went to Oklahoma, where the older ones had gone, and did so without any adult guidance [28]. The same thing was found with storks in Europe [32]. We have mentioned already some of the young shorebirds in the Arctic regions of Canada that migrate successfully after the adults have departed.

Nonsense orientation / A peculiar directional tendency has been found in a few experimental cases. Captured waterfowl—mallards, blue-winged teal, pintails—were taken some distance and released. Their first tendency was to head in a nonmigratory direction. The mallards started off toward the north although it was already winter. The teal seemed to prefer a northwesterly direction, as did the pintails [5]. A similar result was found with mallards caught in a refuge in England and released at various places up to 150 miles distant. They had a strong northwest orientation when first released, regardless of the distance or direction from the refuge and regardless of the season or time of day [25]. One suggestion is that this is a sort of reaction to stress. Being captured, transported and released may involve some stress, but why the stress sends them in a particular direction is still a mystery. There would certainly be no survival value for mallards in heading north in winter under a stressful situation.

Noncelestial Navigation

Wind / Assuming that the bird has inherited a tendency to migrate in a southwesterly direction like his ancestors, there still remains the question of how he determines southwest. We shall look presently at the celestial aspects, such as we ourselves use when traveling by sea or by air. First, however, we shall examine a few other possibilities. One of these is the wind. Frequently there are prevailing winds in a certain direction. It is conceivable that a bird can pick up some cues that enable him to keep on a fairly straight flight with reference to the direction of the wind. Some ornithologists think this is a major factor. It is suggested, for example, that the bird gets its initial direction from the sunrise, notes the wind direction and then flies according to the wind from there on [39]. But it is not clear how well a bird without instruments can tell the direction of, say, a crosswind during flight. The pressure on his feathers or the rest of the body may be fairly constant except when the wind changes in velocity. Nevertheless, chaffinches in Holland were observed to navigate considerably by the wind direction, and if the wind changed slowly, the direction of flight varied accordingly. When the wind dropped, the birds were inclined to stop, as though they were losing their bearings. An elaborate statistical study of data obtained by radar for birds flying across the North Sea indicated that the direction of the wind was a most important factor [21]. It has been pointed out that in spring in the eastern half of the United States, there is a rather continuous system of southerly winds. These may give directional cues to the migrants.

Clouds / There are possibilities even over the open ocean of certain "landmarks," for example, cloudbelts. In July a belt of clouds extends west from San Francisco for some 800 miles. Where there are occasional islands, there will be masses of cumulus clouds built up on the windward slopes of volcanic peaks such as those in Hawaii. These cloudbanks may extend to a 40,000-foot altitude and would be visible for 300 miles to a bird flying at 10,000 feet.

Some earlier theories about bird navigation have been practically discarded now. One was that birds might pick up cues from the magnetic field of the earth, just as we do with a compass. This notion was discredited by experiments with starlings in an observation cage at the migratory season. Large piles of iron were placed near the cage to interfere with the magnetic field, but the starlings still oriented toward the southwest corner of the cage, their normal direction of migration. Similarly, robins and white-throated sparrows were placed in a steel-enclosed room provided with an artificial magnetic field and they still showed the correct orientation in terms of migratory restlessness [11]. Some pigeons had small permanent magnets attached to their wings while the control birds had unmagnetized copper bars of the same size and weight. Presumably the permanent magnets would handicap the birds if they were actually using the earth's magnetic field for navigation. Actually, both groups showed about the same speed and proficiency in homing.

It is somewhat the same story with reference to the mechanical effect resulting from rotation of the earth (Coriolis force). The bird's apparent weight changes according to the direction of flight and the latitude. This force is strongest at the poles and weakest at the equator. There are detailed criticisms of the theory that are too complicated for discussion here. Even if the bird had some sense organ for detecting the changes, it would have to compute its own speed somehow in order to interpret them. It would also have to detect extremely small changes.

There is no known sensory mechanism for receiving such stimuli, but there are rather unusual sensory abilities at various places in the animal kingdom. We have mentioned elsewhere a species of bird that uses a sonar technique. Some snakes are sensitive to infrared heat rays at a considerable distance, and certain moths can smell another moth at a distance of a mile, while bees can respond to polarized light. So it is just possible that someday we may find some unusual sensory capabilities in birds.

Celestial Navigation in Daytime

We may now consider in more detail some of the cues that birds get from the sky. In the daytime the most obvious cue is the sun. There is plenty of evidence that birds use it in finding direction. Some European starlings were kept in a circular cage and records made of their migratory restlessness. In the spring they tended to perch in the northeast part of the cage and in the fall in the southwest, their normal directions of migration. They maintained the correct direction for hours while the sun was moving accordingly. Evidently they adjusted for the position of the sun at different times of day when it was visible through windows in the cage. Then large mirrors were placed outside the windows and so adjusted that they made the sun appear to come from a different direction, for example, 90 degrees to one side of its actual direction. Under these conditions the birds oriented from the apparent sun as if it were the real thing. For instance, in the early morning when the sun was in the east, the birds' tendency to migrate southwest would lead them to perch at something over 100 degrees to the right of the sun. Then when the sun was displaced, they perched at something over 100 degrees to the right of the "new" sun in the early morning [15]. The same result was found with several other species, including meadowlarks, warblers, red-backed shrikes and homing pigeons. If the windows in the cage were dense and minimized the sun's light, the orientation was less definite.

Other experiments were made by training birds in a cage to go in a certain compass direction for food. Around the periphery of their cage, starlings had food dishes which all looked alike, but only one actually contained food. Let us say that this one was always south. The birds presently learned to go in that direction at any time of day, making appropriate correction for the movement of the sun. There were no cues from inside the cage because it was of uniform construction throughout. Similarly, blue-winged teal and green-winged teal had 12 little cage doors through which they might go to seek water, but only one actually led to water. The teal could see the open sky through the top of the cage, and they learned to go in the correct compass direction when the sun was visible. Cloud cover interfered with this, and they also had trouble with the clear sky before sunrise and after sunset [13].

Again, homing pigeons trained in a cage in North Carolina and then taken to Brazil and tested there in a similar cage, did not make allowance for the local sun but acted as if it were the Carolina sun [35].

Granted that the bird uses cues from the sun there is the question of how it does so. Presumably to some extent merely the direction of the sun affects the bird's tendency to go toward it or at a certain angle to one side. This, however, is not a sufficient explanation for all types of orientation. Another variable is the fact that as we go farther north, the sun does not get as high above the horizon, even at its noon maximum.

Let's take an oversimplified example of a homing pigeon released south or north of home at noon. Hopefully, it can remember the height of the sun at noon at its home location. Now suppose the bird is released where the sun does not seem as high at noon as it does at home. Actually the bird must be north of home so it flies toward the sun, that is, south. Conversely, if the sun looks higher than it does at home at noon, the bird must fly away from the sun, thus, going north. The bird cannot figure this out in so many words, but it may have some awareness of differences in height and have an instinctive tendency to go toward the lower sun or away from the higher sun.

We cannot expect the bird to wait until noon for all this, as in our oversimplified example. However, if one observes the sun for some minutes in the morning, he can see it moving up slowly along a curve. It may be possible to extrapolate this curve and estimate about where the sun would be at its high point at noon. If a bird can do that, then it might be possible to make the comparison in the manner just described. Some experimenters believe that this is how the bird actually does orient itself [26]. At least it can be shown that the sense organs in the bird's retina are capable of making discriminations of the small magnitude involved in noting the difference in height of the sun at areas 50 miles apart in a north-south flight.

Celestial Navigation at Night

At night the most obvious possibility for navigation is the stars. Navigation is interfered with at night by cloudy weather just as it is during the day. Those mallard ducks taken away from their nesting location and released with small lights on their legs headed in the correct direction when it was clear, but not when it was overcast. If the sky was rather cloudy but the moon was still visible, that did not help; it appeared that they needed the stars [4]. Tracking birds over the North Sea by radar indicated that on cloudy nights they did not migrate at all; if they were aloft and clouds closed in on them, they began to mill around aimlessly. Similarly with the radar tracking at Cape Cod of migrants, some disorientation was associated with overcast. The orientation of bobolinks in cages at the time of migration showed no clear tendency when the sky was obscured by clouds.

A further study indicated that this tendency was "built in," as we have assumed all along. Certain warblers and chickadees were taken from the nest at about nine days of age and reared in captivity. Their living quarters were such that they never saw the sky. Presently they were put in an activity cage to check migratory restlessness at the appropriate season, and they took the appropriate direction when the sky was clear. However, it is to be noted that they had never seen the sky before, so whatever tendency they had to orient by the sky was innate [33].

A further check on celestial navigation by the stars was made by putting the activity cage in a planetarium. With this it is possible to show the star pattern for any time of the year [34]. Several types of birds—warblers, white-throated sparrows and shrikes—were used. In the season when they would normally migrate southeast, if the overhead stars in the planetarium were set to look like the normal sky at that season, the birds oriented correctly. If the planetarium stars were shifted somewhat, they were less well oriented. Although it was autumn, when they would normally collect on the south side of the cage, if the experimenter gave them the spring sky in the planetarium, there was confusion. In responding to the sky they tended to go toward the north; however, it was the season when they *should* go south, perhaps in response to internal stimuli. The result was conflict and some of them became completely disoriented. Incidentally, it was shown that they could orient correctly in the planetarium without the planets or the moon being illuminated, which suggests that some of the fixed stars were involved.

INTERNAL "CLOCK"

IT is apparent that successful navigation requires some kind of awareness of time. In our case we need a chronometer, especially when computing longitude. Quite a few animals have internal "clocks" of some sort, and this has been shown in the case of certain birds although we do not know what the exact mechanism is. Let's take a human analogy to get the general picture. Suppose I get up about 6 A.M. If I see the sun in the east and want to head south, I go 90 degrees to the right of the sun. However, when I have been up six hours, I head directly toward the sun if I want to go south. But suppose I got up at 6 A.M. and erroneously *thought* it was noon; I then would head toward the sun, mistakenly going east.

Something of this sort was found with starlings trained to go in a certain compass direction in the cage in order to get food, as described earlier. They could do it throughout the day and allow for the position of the sun. Let us suppose that the food box is always located in the southerly direction. If the bird awakes at 6 A.M., when the sun is in the east, the bird would head 90 degrees to the right of the sun to get the food in the south. After he has been up six hours, at noon he would head *directly* toward the sun.

Now let's reset his "clock." We turn on the lights in his living quarters at midnight so the bird awakens six hours earlier than usual. Now, when he is put in the test cage at 6 A.M., he has already been awake six hours and that means he is to go directly toward the sun for the food, which he actually does. He goes east, just as the man did who arose at six and "thought" it was noon. What the starling "thought" is problematical, but objectively it acted as it normally did at the supposed time [15]. When the experiment was checked with various directions and various settings of the clock, the results corroborated the principle just described. Similar results were found with pigeons going to a certain compass direction in the cage and even homing from a distance. The direction they took depended on the way the clock had been reset [36].

The celestial navigation of birds becomes a little more remarkable if we realize that a human navigator requires an astronomical almanac; he must know the date and the time very accurately; he needs instruments that will "shoot" the sun or the stars. How birds do it we do not yet know, but they manage somehow, and it is not something that they learn in school, either. It is built in. Heredity apparently does a remarkable job for birds in some situations.

CHAPTER VI

Aspects of Learning

Supplementing Instinctive Behavior

While their behavior to a major degree involves instinctive factors, birds do learn on occasion. Sometimes the instinctive tendency is incomplete and does not furnish the entire behavior pattern. Flying is an instance. Birds instinctively go through the flying motions when they have adequate muscular development, but they must perfect the performance to some extent. A young albatross, for example, flies after a fashion and then does a crash landing on the beach and slides along on its belly. After a little experience it makes a more graceful landing. Similarly, the ability to fly in a high wind improves some with practice—but the instinctive tendency to fly was there at the outset.

Again, birds instinctively forage for food, but they learn the locus of a particular cornfield or back-yard feeder. (If one maintains a feeder in the autumn until migration time, he should continue to stock that feeder through the winter since some of the birds may have abandoned migration in favor of wintering where there is a good food supply. If one discontinues maintenance of the feeder in midwinter, the birds may have lost the tendency to migrate by that time and are in for a tough winter.) In the north country when the population of lemmings is greatly reduced, the snowy owls, which depend upon them for food almost exclusively, are in a bad way and come south to the United States and learn to use the rodents there.

Nest building is largely instinctive. The red-winged blackbirds originally nested in marshes, but when these dried up, they learned to use alfalfa fields. So while instincts are generally inflexible, a modest amount of modification is possible and may prevent a catastrophe. Ability to learn in the sense of modifying these instinctive responses has some survival value.

Trial and Error

We may now consider some learning mechanisms, *i.e.*, how the learning actually takes place. The old standby is the trial-and-error method, in which the animal tries various responses to a situation. The successful responses are rewarded (*i.e.* reinforced), and the incorrect ones punished. In the laboratory if we want to teach an animal to go into the left of two doors, we give him food if he enters the left door and an electric shock if he goes into the right. Similarly, a bird picks up a caterpillar and gets a pleasant taste and thus learns to pick up that kind of caterpillar when hungry. If the taste is unpleasant, the bird learns to avoid such caterpillars.

While nest building is an innate tendency, the bird may learn that some materials are too stiff and unsuitable. If it becomes impossible to weave a particular bit of material into the nest, something akin to dissatisfaction will result and the material is dropped. When other materials are used successfully, there may be something like satisfaction. We cannot be sure about these subjective aspects. But objectively the behavior is reinforced and the bird learns. We mentioned earlier how the weaverbird perfects his skill in the actual manipulation of the materials used. Again, a woodpecker in an area where there are no dead trees in which to drill holes for a nest or noctural roost tries live trees. They do not chip very readily, so it tackles a telephone pole, which works better, and it uses poles in the future.

Timing of reinforcement / Reinforcement must occur at the right time so it can be associated with the act that is being learned. A good instance deals with learning to avoid a trap. Two general types of traps are in common use. In one the bird steps on a platform and trips a trigger that lets a door drop behind him. In the other type he goes into a simple maze or at least goes around several corners, eats the bait and presently finds himself confined. Then he gets excited and dashes hither and yon. Actually, if he kept calm he could walk right out the way he came in, but he seldom does so because of the emotional overtones.

The interesting point in the present connection is that birds learn to avoid the type of trap where they step on a trigger but do not learn very readily to avoid the maze type. The reason for this difference is the time at which the "punishment" or negative reinforcement occurs. When a bird enters and immediately steps on something and the door slams behind him, the experience is unpleasant and is associated with entering because it occurred immediately after he did enter. In the other type of trap, however, the bird goes in and eats grain or something for a while and then somewhat later discovers that he is trapped and gets excited. However, this reinforcement is not associated with the actual entering because it came so much later. This situation is a good deal like the youngster whose mother arranges to have father punish him when he gets home, by which time it is difficult to associate the belated punishment with the crime, and the punishment usually is not as effective as if it occurred immediately after the act was perpetrated.

RECOGNITION / Some trial-and-error learning takes place in the field of recognition. The bird may use landmarks in order to locate its nest. In one instance there was a box near the nest that seemed like a possible cue. The experimenter moved the box while the bird was absent, and when the bird returned, it went to the new location of the box and did not find the nest. Obviously the box was the critical landmark. But presently the bird learned to find the nest regardless of the location of the box [21 p. 57].

We raised the question earlier of birds' recognizing their young, which is to some extent a matter of learning. When a brood of herring gulls had just been hatched, one could introduce a foreign nestling and the parents would accept the intruder. But if a foster youngster was introduced a week later, he was rejected and usually killed. By that time the parents had learned certain cues whereby they recognized their own young.

PECK ORDER / An interesting instance of trial-and-error learning is involved in establishing the peck order. Essentially the bird tries one adversary after another. Winning a fight is positive reinforcement and the bird learns that it is superior to that particular opponent, and losing a fight is negative reinforcement and it learns to whom it is subordinate. The ultimate hierarchy depends on individual differences in aggressiveness, which will be discussed in detail in Chapter X.

Conditioning

Conditioning is a type of learning that occurs quite frequently under laboratory conditions, but it probably does not play as big a role with wild birds as does trial and error. We described the basic principles in Chapter II in connection with measurement of hearing range. The bird was stimulated by an electric shock, whereupon it jumped off the perch (unconditioned response). Then in a series of trials a sound was presented along with the shock; the bird continued to jump, but presently the shock could be omitted and the bird jumped at the sound alone (conditioned response).

In another experiment previously described, ducks in a pen were frightened if a hawklike cardboard silhouette was towed overhead. Eventually the ducks showed uneasiness when the experimenters started installing the pulleys for the day's experiment—*before* the model was visible. This was another case of conditioning.

The same mechanism may be involved in the young bird learning from the parents some source of danger. Suppose the young one is chased under the bushes by the parents when a man appears. Initially it is frightened by the parent, but the man is in view and presently the fear becomes conditioned to the man. As an instance, on a boat on the Great Lakes the cooks threw out refuse that the gulls enjoyed. Presently the birds learned to gather around the boat when anyone appeared in a white coat such as the cooks wore.

The writer had some cowbirds that entered his large decoy trap repeatedly. The corn used as bait (or food) was kept in a large metal container with a lid. Some of the birds became conditioned to the rattle of the lid and if hungry would fly rapidly to the vicinity of the container whenever the lid was opened but before the food was visible.

Habituation

Habituation is a negative type of learning in which a bird merely gets used to something and does not react as it did at its first experience with the object. This matter of learning not to respond is a common result of frequent exposure to loud sounds or sudden movements that are actually harmless. At the outset birds in the yard may become alarmed at a car starting or a person walking out to the garage. Presently they do not fly from the feeder every time the car owner appears. Birds may even show some habituation to stimuli that are presented deliberately to frighten them, and it does not take the birds very long to become habituated. An example of such habituation involved carbide caps used to scare starlings from a particular area where they roosted at night. Presently the starlings did not even look toward the source of the explosion 200 feet away but merely went on with their "conversation." There is an obvious economy in all this: the birds do not waste a lot of time responding to unimportant or meaningless stimuli.

Habituation may be seen in some nesting situations, such as the bird that builds its nest on the berm or margin, of a busy highway and soon adjusts to the harmless passing traffic, the robin that nests in the pump of an oil derrick, where the nest goes up and down about one yard with every stroke. In one instance, certain warblers (blue-winged, Kirtland), reared by hand and carefully observed, at the age of two or three weeks were apparently frightened by all white cabbage butterflies and crouched or hopped away; a week later they ignored the butterflies or ate them. Similarly, birds learn that certain animals like a dog or a chipmunk are not dangerous [1, p. 142].

One study afforded a bit of quantitative data on habituation. A British sparrowlike bird, the chaffinch, was confined in an aviary with a small owl of a species that would not harm it for a 20-minute period each day. The chaffinch has an alarm note that sounds like *chink*. The observer counted the number of *chinks* that occurred in each 20-minute interval. On the fifth day, the *chinks* were only 30 per cent as frequent in the test period as they were on the first day; after 12 days they were only 10 per cent as frequent [7].

TAMENESS / In some examples of habituation, described as tameness, situations that ordinarily frighten birds cease to do so. Common instances are the behaviors of birds at some refuge where they are fed and protected. A zoo may have ducks that are loosely attached to the zoo, not kept in pens but living in a nearby river and fed periodically. Under those circumstances wild birds such as Canada geese may come along, essentially decoyed by the ducks, and share the food. Presently they may get so accustomed to the situation that they come in regularly and may even stay in the vicinity the year round.

There are also cases where wild birds have been reared as pets. The process is more expeditious if the bird is taken when very young. Frequently somebody has a pet crow that circulates around the yard when the family is sitting out, pulls at shoelaces, perches on shoulders, and the like. Something resembling tameness may occur on a temporary basis, although we have to be careful in interpretation. Some wild birds when sitting on the nest with eggs or young will continue to sit there even though a person approaches to the point at which the bird ordinarily would leave. There have been cases where one could come up and touch the bird gently. However, this was not entirely a case of getting habituated to people, because the tendency to protect the eggs or the young was quite strong at that time. After nesting was over, the bird would not let a person come so close. Another case already mentioned was that of the birds that use hair to build a nest at the appropriate time approaching a human being and trying to pull out some hair. This never occurred at other times of the year.

Tameness in the above sense is something that is learned, and is not the same thing as lack of fear of man, for example, because one has had no experience with him. Puffins learn to avoid gulls and other predators because they are around all the time, but a man who makes a business of catching puffins with a hook on the end of a long stick is able to approach. The birds are tame with reference to man because the species has had almost no experience with people. Furthermore, the individual bird that is captured by the man cannot learn avoidance because he is killed [14]. Similarly, an albatross on an uninhabited island has developed no fear of man, and one can approach and touch it on the nest or even lift it slightly in order to look at the eggs underneath [10].

Individual birds probably differ somewhat in the readiness with which they habituate to situations and human beings. These differences come under the general notion of personality, which we shall discuss in a later chapter.

Insight Learning

Sometimes insight is regarded as a category of learning. The clearest instances of insight occur when, in a difficult situation, the solution suddenly "pops up," such as when we are working on a puzzle and it suddenly dawns on us that we should follow some particular system. Sometimes we attempt to evaluate the intelligence of an individual or a species in terms of the extent to which it employs insight learning.

With reference to birds we need to be especially cautious in this connection. They do some things that look rather ingenious, but we should not explain them as insight unless we have to. Perhaps the nearest thing to insight that has been reported is the seeming use of "tools" by finches in the Galapagos Islands [13]. The little woodpecker finch there uses a small stick or a cactus spine to probe for insects in holes or crevices that are too deep for its bill. When the insect runs out, the bird drops its tool and grabs the insect. Many individual birds of this species show this unique behavior, and it is tempting to interpret this behavior as insight. It is possible that all of these finches could employ insight in learning to use these tools, but it is much more probable that this behavior was a mutation somewhere back in the ancestry with obvious survival value and thus could have evolved in conventional fashion.

Another instance of apparent insight involves a green heron that put bits of bread into the water and ate the fish that were attracted to the "bait," also driving away other birds that came in after the bread. One ornithologist interpreted this behavior as "intentionally using the bread as fish bait." It may have been [15]. Other heron-type birds have been observed catching small fish that were nibbling at a bit of bread or other food that happened to be floating in the water. However, the present heron actually put the food there, which was an additional step and possibly insightful. This same bird did one more interesting thing. While it was watching the piece of bread where it floated, some small fish broke the water several feet to one side. Thereupon the heron picked up the bit of bread and put it over near where the fish had broken the water. Most any good fisherman would be inclined to assume that the bird knew what it was doing.

A Finnish ornithologist reported a crow that learned to reel in the lines where men were fishing through the ice. It would hold the line in its bill while walking backward a distance, then it would walk on the line toward the hole in the ice to get another grip and walk backward again. In this way it eventually got the fish [8]. It would, of course, be possible to learn a behavior of this sort by trying different things with the fish line and eventually hitting on the solution. This could result from a general adaptability that suggests a fair amount of intelligence. In other situations crows have been reputed to be rather adaptable, as in seeking out alternate sources of food when their normal supply runs out, as contrasted with some birds that starve under those circumstances.

But we should note that it is possible to teach the animal a behavior that looks like using tools to us but is really fairly simple for the animal. Birds have been taught deliberately to secure food on the end of a string by pulling the string with the beak, then holding the string with the claws while getting another grip with the beak. In the sixteenth century, European goldfinches kept as pets were taught this trick—pulling either food or a dish of water up a slight incline. In fact, they were called water drawers. When some finches and canaries were taught a similar trick under laboratory conditions, their improvement was gradual rather than showing a sudden insight. This study tends to minimize the insight aspect at least for this kind of performance [22].

Imitation / A type of learning that is usually considered to be of a rather high order is learning by imitation. There are a few inconclusive hints of this type of learning with birds. To cite a single instance, some green finches were taught to discriminate between two visual patterns in connection with feeding tests. Then some untrained birds were confronted with the same situation. Some had as partners in the situation birds already trained and some had untrained partners. The experimental birds with untrained partners took longer to learn to discriminate than did those with trained partners [11]. Whether this was an example of imitation in the strict sense or merely social facilitation is debatable. The presence of the trained partner eating might be enough to stimulate the learner to greater activity in the food situation.

Insight learning on the part of birds is challenging but difficult of interpretation. The use of tools comes about the nearest to insight of any of the behaviors reported. Perhaps we should accept cautiously a few instances, especially with crows, where there seems to be an ability to learn that is quite adaptable and to some extent intelligent. If there are cases of insight learning in birds, they are few and far between.

Permanence of Learning

Much learned behavior persists for a time because the performance is periodically reinforced. If a bird learns the location of a particular feeder and goes there repeatedly, it gets food reinforcement throughout the season, but there is the question of whether it will remember the specific location if it returns to the vicinity the following year. We remember many things for life, but little is known about birds in this respect. If they return to the same food source the next season we cannot rule out the possibility that they learned it all over again rather than remembering it immediately.

One incident with some crows does suggest a fairly high degree of retention. A tame owl was placed on a particular tree in the woods directly on the route of crows during their spring migration. As usual they ganged up on the owl, gathering around, diving toward him and making a lot of noise without actually injuring him. Six months later, on fall migration, several crows went to that same tree where the owl had been and demonstrated aggressively at the same branch. Probably they were the same crows and remembered the spot in some fashion. The exact nature of their recall is anybody's guess. We do this sort of thing sometimes by conjuring up an actual image or picture of the object we are recalling. Whether crows have imagery nobody knows [19, p. 44].

Helps in Learning

Birds sometimes give their youngsters a little help in a learning situation. This may be a bit drastic, as with the grebe, which gets the young one on its back, swims out to deep water and submerges so that the juvenile will have to swim. However, the adult merely provides the situation in which the youngster must try to swim. No actual teaching is involved. There are more indications of tuition with reference to feeding. Young birds may learn the location of a food source by association with adults. They follow their parents on a feeding expedition and thus are led to food or water. The question, however, is what the young bird actually learns. The chick pecks where the parent does and thus gets some grain, which looks at the moment like imitation. If, however, there is a piece of lettuce available and a person taps it with his finger, the chick comes over and eats the lettuce. Certainly the human is not eating the lettuce as an imitiative source. More likely the movement or the tapping sound merely draws the chick's attention to the lettuce. Once the attention is drawn to the food, instinct will take care of the rest [3].

There are cases, however, where it is quite clear that the bird did learn something from the parent even though we cannot be sure of the details. A population of pheasants was studied. Some of them were trapped wild birds that had developed in the wild, presumably with their parents. Others were game-farm birds that had hatched and grown up without benefit of wild parents. Both populations were banded and released. Many of the birds were shot by hunters and the bands recovered. A larger proportion of the bands that came back were from the game-farm birds than from the birds that had been reared in the wild. In other words, those with the wild upbringing eluded the hunters and survived to a greater extent. It is probable that this difference was due to behaviors that one group had learned from their wild parents, although we cannot pinpoint the nature of those behaviors or how the parents taught them.

Training by Man

Many domestic animals have been trained for various purposes. This has not been the case with domestic birds to any great extent because all they are supposed to do is raise families and eat a lot so that they will themselves be edible—neither of which functions requires any training. However, some birds have been used in connection with hunting. Trained falcons are released when some other bird is flying over, whereupon the falcon goes and captures him, usually by getting above the prey and then diving. This sport existed in Persia by 1700 B.C. and in China by 1200 B.C. The details of training a falcon need not concern us here.

We mentioned earlier the use of cormorants by fishermen in the Orient. Diving for the fish is largely instinctive, but sometimes the birds receive a little training also. They learn to go overboard at a whistle and to return to the boat after resurfacing at another whistle. It is said that they learn more readily in the presence of trained birds, but no actual data are available [16, p. 58].

Birds have been taught tricks for entertainment purposes. We mentioned the goldfinches in the Middle Ages trained to pull up a bit of food on the end of a string. Similarly, in England titmice were taught to pull up a peanut. But starlings and robins (English species) seemed unable to learn this particular trick.

Some people are in the business of training animals, including chickens, to do stunts at zoos, fairs or in store windows. The following instance shows how an instinctive tendency that cropped up in the course of the training was capitalized upon. In the ultimate performance a chicken in the store window pulled a loop that started a simple recorded tune (jukebox) and then got on a platform and scratched (danced). In the original training the owners taught the bird, after it had pulled the loop, to hop on the platform and stay for 15 seconds, whereupon it would be reinforced with food. However, when over half of the chickens got on the platform, they started to scratch. This is a common instinctive pattern with a species that often scratches for food. So the trainers insured this scratching behavior by rewarding the birds when they did it that way. Thus they developed a better "act." If the publicity indicated that the chickens were going to "dance," the observers outside the window would interpret the instinctive scratching as dancing in response to the music [2].

Various studies of birds' learning have been made under laboratory conditions. One problem investigated was how early in life birds could actually learn to avoid something, for instance, an electric shock. Some chickens at the age of two days were able to do this, and most of them could handle the situation by four days [9].

Birds have on occasion been taught to find their way through a maze or labyrinth. Various perching birds were put through a fairly complicated and widely used maze, the Hampton Court maze. They required from 20 to 50 trials to learn to negotiate it [18].

Imprinting

Nature / Imprinting is a special case of learning that we seldom notice unless something goes wrong. We noted in Chapter IV that as a young duckling matures it reaches a critical age when it is ready to follow a moving object and become attached to it. The moving object usually is the parent duck but there have been instances of a duck getting imprinted to people.

Imprinting of this sort is important to the bird because it often determines who will be his relatives in the social sense. To be sure, they usually are relatives in the genetic sense also, because the bird generally is imprinted to his own species. But on occasion a young bird gets imprinted to a different species. The logical outcome of the resulting association with that species is eventual breeding across species lines. Hybrids do occur, especially with ducks, but when the hybrid tries to breed, there may be difficulty. Courtship usually involves some ritual in the way of posture, position of head or wings or tail, and this posture pattern is inherited as a species characteristic. If a male hybrid inherits, say, the head posture from one parent and the tail posture from the other, the combination may not be "correct" for either species, and an eligible female from either species would not be interested. To be sure, there are a few cases where a hybrid interbreeds, such as the Brewster warbler, but only a few. Thanks to imprinting, the bird spends most of its life with its own species. Without this mechanism there might well be chaos—especially for the bird watchers—and interspecific promiscuity.

Imprinting lends itself readily to experimental study. We may expose young birds in the laboratory to an assortment of moving objects such as boxes, balls, alarm clocks, toys and bird models. This may be done at different ages and on different schedules. We record quantitatively their tendency to follow the test object. At a later time we expose them to the same object again and determine if they are still attached to it. Some of the problems investigated by this method will now be discussed.

Critical Period / A major characteristic of imprinting is the critical period of development in which imprinting is possible, for before and after this period, imprinting is impossible. This critical period varies considerably among species. For domestic chickens it is from 13 to 16 hours after hatching; for mallard ducklings it is about the same but can take place up to an age of 72 hours; Pekin ducks are best at eight to ten hours but can still manage it on the fourth day of life. The critical period for ring doves is age seven to nine days, which reflects the immaturity of this species at time of hatching. The young spend several days in the nest being fed by their parents before they are able to get around themselves. By contrast, chickens and ducklings are able to run about as soon as they are dried off [6]. Since imprinting involves following something, it is unlikely to occur until the chick can locomote.

The earliest date at which imprinting can occur, as just implied, reflects differences in maturity. Locomotion is an obvious requirement but more subtle aspects of maturity may make a difference of a few days. What determines the terminal point of the critical period is not clear. One suggestion is that the belated test object may produce a fear response. Some birds do become more wary as they get older and when they first encounter, say, a colored ball, may shy away from it. While this explanation seems plausible with reference to balls, boxes and the like, it is not necessarily true regarding wariness toward the parent duck. Actually, we have no evidence regarding the age beyond which imprinting to the parent is impossible. As far as the writer knows, no one has taken the trouble to determine this in the laboratory. In the wild the usual imprinting to the parent takes place quite early unless some abortive stimulus comes along before the parent.

Species Differences / We do not know too much about the readiness with which various species may be imprinted. Most of the experimental work has been with ducks, geese and domestic fowl, species that are readily available and also move about on the ground at an early age. By the time species like robins are ready to follow something, they do it on the wing rather than on foot. Thus they could not be imprinted to a human being. It is possible that imprinting does occur in flight, but we cannot observe it because everything is happening so rapidly. As far as observations and experiments go, many species do have this method of learning, but whether species differ in the readiness with which they do this and whether some cannot do it at all we do not know.

Permanence / Imprinting may appear to be quite permanent. A bird that starts following its own species about continues to do so throughout life, and there are likewise some reported cases of a duck following a man for a lifetime, but we should be cautious about calling this permanent imprinting. If the duck follows a man who feeds it, it is subjected to reinforced learning. Similarly, if it follows other ducks there may be some rewards. The mother bird for instance leads the youngster to food. When effort was made experimentally to eliminate the reward, the imprinting effect decreased. Pekin ducks were imprinted to a cardboard cube but never rewarded for following it. After 15 days they lost interest completely. In a similar experiment, coots decreased their following tendency in seven to eight weeks and lost it altogether by the time they were mature. Also, there are other factors besides imprinting that keep the birds of a species together. Flocking as an instinctive tendency is discussed elsewhere.

Emotional Aspects / It is probable that a young bird in the presence of its mother experiences something analogous to the comfort or security that a human infant feels. It is possible, also, that even the imprinted inanimate mother may contribute to the emotional satisfaction of the young bird. There was some evidence of this in one experiment in which young chicks were imprinted to an artificial mother made out of cloth. Presently the young birds were placed with the cloth mother in a test cage where they were disturbed by a doorbell that sounded intermittently for three minutes. After the bell ceased, they were kept five minutes longer in the box and their distress calls were recorded on tape and counted. Control chicks were placed in the same cage on the same schedule with the same cloth mother, but they had not been imprinted to this cloth mother. On the average, the imprinted birds gave 38 distress calls per minute and the nonimprinted birds 89. It appeared that imprinting even on an artificial parent somehow reduced the stress [20].

Effort Involved / There is a suggestion that greater effort during imprinting facilitates the process. If the bird follows the object by walking up an incline, it imprints a little more readily. This effort seems more important than the actual length of time exposed to the test object, although some experimenters are not convinced of this [6]. Chickens even did pretty well when they were dragged after the ball to which they were being imprinted and their main effort was in resisting the pull [17]. Again, a mild electric shock in the alley just prior to the test or during the test led to more vigorous following and increased strength of imprinting. It is possible that the following tends to reduce anxiety, as indicated in the preceding section.

Other Reinforcements / Another element that has been found to reinforce the process of imprinting is an accompanying sound. While Pekin ducklings were being imprinted to a moving model of a mallard duck, a recorded call of a woodduck sometimes was presented along with the moving model. In one series of experiments 40 per cent of the ducklings followed the silent model and 70 per cent the vocal model [4]. It is possible, however, that they were being imprinted somewhat to the sound rather than having it merely reinforce the moving object, for in some later tests with the sound alone the birds did show a tendency to go toward it [12].

As suggested above, there has been little indication of imprinting except in the case of following a moving object. There may be other imprinted behaviors that we do not know about, but at least this special learning situation serves a useful purpose in the early behavior of many birds. There is considerable literature on experimental imprinting [5].

We have now considered the principal types of response of individual birds, both unlearned and learned. We shall now turn to the social situation where birds are reacting primarily to other birds.

CHAPTER VII

Social Behavior of Birds

T*hus far we have been discussing the* bird primarily as an individual. The bird reacts to food and water, rain and sunshine, heat and cold; but it also reacts to other birds, and that is where social psychology comes in. To be sure, we have touched on it here and there, but now we shall look at it more specifically. Human beings are overwhelmingly social animals—we live in families, we join organizations, we play (or watch) games and we fight wars. Birds' lives are social to a lesser degree but still enough so to warrant some discussion.

Grouping

The most obvious instance of social behavior is birds' simply going some place together in a group. Anyone with a feeder or birdbath has seen modest manifestations of this. More dramatic is the sizable flock, say, of starlings and various blackbirds. Thousands may gather for the night in a clump of trees or on the ledges of a downtown building.

Species' Differences / Species differ in their grouping behavior. We seldom see a group of hawks soaring together, but flocks of crows are common and we often see large numbers of ducks or geese on the water or in the air. Some of their behavior may merely be sticking together during migration, but if they remain in one place even for a short time, we may observe the same grouping tendency as during migration. A good example of this is to be found among shorebirds. One generally sees a spotted sandpiper feeding alone, as is true of the solitary sandpiper, who is well named. But the yellowlegs and pectoral sandpipers arrive in flocks, the latter having been counted in flocks of from 25 to 150. The flock itself is relatively stable, and there is little exchange between groups. If two flocks join in the air, they usually separate before landing; if there is a composite landing, they separate shortly. These tendencies were noted during detailed and prolonged observations from a car parked on a dike in a marsh. The stability of a flock was determined by counting it repeatedly, and the observer was able to recognize some individual members by plumage or behavior [15].

The European partridge operates in a much smaller group—usually 5 to 15. This may simply be a single family constituting a covey, or it may also include a few others who were unsuccessful in establishing their own family [17]. The social stimulus or actual cue that keeps the flock together is not necessarily visual. In deep woods or dense shrubbery the birds respond to each other's calls. Otherwise one might get "lost" as far as the flock was concerned.

Own Brood / With some species social behavior begins pretty early in life. Young ducks apparently get attached socially to the other members in their own little group, which may be advantageous in some species such as the diving ducks, where the parents desert the young before they can actually fly, and is certainly safer in any case. One instance has been reported of a young mallard that showed social inclinations on the very day it was hatched. The bird was hatched in an incubator, and on its first day was put in with two five-day-old redhead ducks. These latter attacked the young mallard persistently, but when it was "rescued" and taken away, it gave distress calls until it was put back with its tormentors. Evidently the drive to be with other ducks was stronger than the desire to be unmolested [8].

It should be pointed out that this getting together does not necessarily mean physical contact. Cliff swallows are very gregarious and stay together in sizable groups, but when they perch on the wires, they are about four inches apart. One can see and hear its friend but can extend its wings with impunity. As noted elsewhere, this tendency to spread out slightly may be advantageous in foraging as the birds do not all land on the same bit of food simultaneously.

Roosts / Another manifestation of getting together is roosting for the night. Frequently, "blackbirds" such as red-wings, cowbirds, starlings and grackles gather for the night in a patch of woods. About sunset they start coming in from all directions, and the last ones arrive just before dark. There is a good deal of calling back and forth, but presently they quiet down. At daylight there are some calls and a little flying about in the roost, and then groups take off so that in a half hour or so the roost is empty. This behavior is more noticeable in the fall, when many of the other birds already have gone south, but it takes place to some extent at other times of year. Robins sometimes gather together to pass the night in a small clump of trees, and crows do likewise and are often conspicuous when proceeding in large numbers toward a roost some miles distant. Sometimes a roost is homogeneous, with only crows or robins, and sometimes heterogeneous, including several species. This group roosting to a certain extent may be merely seeking shelter simultaneously in a convenient place, but from the chatter going on while the roost is gathering, it would seem that there must be social overtones.

COMMUNAL SLEEPING / Some species sleep together in much smaller numbers but nevertheless show social behavior. Rails, coots and gallinules build platforms above the water on which several members of the species sleep collectively, a practice that may have developed from their tendency to build platforms on which to put nests and then to sleep in the nests [25]. Six members of a species of toucan in Central America that roosts in old woodpecker holes were observed spending the night together in one hole. With a species of barbet in Costa Rica, 16 were found sleeping in one hole [26].

COMMUNAL NESTING / Mention was made earlier of communal nesting. This is most spectacular where we find large colonies of seabirds roosting on the rocks. The concentration is not always due to a shortage of space, because frequently there will be plenty of suitable space left vacant. Of course, there may be subtle reasons why it does not look suitable to the birds, but it does seem as if they "prefer" to nest in groups. Usually they do not actually help each other, and each family remains essentially intact. However, there may be some mutual warning of danger and mutual defense against predators. There are also occasional instances where everybody seems to incubate the eggs at random [9].

Other species that normally build their nests on widely separated territories may nest close together contrary to the usual pattern, as has been found with a few goldfinches and with the Kirtland warbler. Even grackles have been observed to establish 15 or 20 nests fairly close together although even then each grackle has a small individual territory [11]. This is nothing like the degree of communality found in the nesting of some ocean birds.

MASS ACTIVITIES / Another instance of group behavior that might be mentioned is a sort of mass demonstration. Some 150 avocets crowded on a muddy islet about 12 feet in diameter. The entire mass revolved slowly, like the hands of a clock, as if the members were marching half-time. If some were crowded into the water, others flew in to take their places. The action did not appear to be a courtship manifestation, and the birds were not feeding during the process. Presumably it had some relation to flocking tendencies, but the reason for the routine was not clear [14, p. 163].

The trumpeters in the tropics (related to the crane) participate in what resembles a community dance. First they clear a dancing area, pull out all the vegetation and scratch up the dirt. Then two birds go into the center, prance, strut and jump into the air. Presently they are replaced by two others, and there is considerable variation in the "steps" of different pairs. Then still others get into the act and eventually the whole group is dancing. This performance occurs usually at sunrise or at sunset. It is not a courtship manifestation because it occurs at all seasons of the year, and in one case specifically after the young had all been reared and had gone away [28].

GENETIC ASPECT

THE explanation of social behavior may be a bit complicated, though some of it doubtless results from innate tendencies. Biologists often talk of a "gregarious instinct," and the predilection for getting together could have developed, like other innate tendencies, by natural selection. Keeping in a flock can have survival value in that it affords some protection against predators. A hawk seldom dives into the midst of a flock of ducks but is more inclined to pick off stragglers. Pectoral sandpipers, when threatened by a predator, have been observed to fly in a compact flock [15]. Another survival feature of flocking is that the group may locate food more readily than if the members foraged individually.

It may be noted that the individual bird is not uniformly social; in fact he may, on occasion, be very unsocial. In the spring the male sets up a nesting territory and chases other males out of sight, but when nesting is over and the family has gone, he begins to get more tolerant of other members of his species. However, this asocial behavior may be just as genetic as the social behavior the rest of the year and implement a necessary phase of the breeding cycle.

External Factors

Instinct may not be the whole story in flocking behavior, and some external situation may bring the birds together quite apart from any tendency to form a flock for its own sake. If water is scarce elsewhere, it is obvious when they gather at a waterhole, for instance; they just happen to get thirsty at about the same time and that brings them in rather than any desire to meet the other folks. Still it is possible that after their thirst is quenched they stay around awhile to socialize. Similarly, if food is concentrated some place, the birds tend to concentrate. After grain has been harvested and appreciable amounts spilled here and there through the fields, the English sparrows often gather. They seem intent on the food and not on each other unless several reach for the same morsel simultaneously.

Another case of getting together for obviously external reasons is the situation in which there is some common danger (predator). Most birds seek refuge under such conditions, and if there is only one safe bit of cover in the vicinity, naturally, that is where they all gather.

Modifications of Social Behavior

Even though much social behavior is genetic and appears very early, nevertheless it can on occasion be modified somewhat. For instance, one group of young chicks was reared in complete isolation for their first four weeks while others were reared in pairs and still others in flocks. At the end of the period all were observed individually in a test cage at one end of which was another small cage containing a chick of about the same age—the stimulus chick. This stimulus was visible through a coarse wire screen. A section of the floor next to the partition was hinged so that if the test chick stepped on it, the platform made an electric contact which actuated a pen recording on a moving tape. The notion was that the more gregarious the test chick the more time he would spend on the end near the stimulus chick.

The chicks reared in isolation spent less time in this manner than did those who had had social contacts during their first four weeks. The isolatees at the outset spent about 25 per cent of their time at the social end of the test cage while the others spent 55 per cent. Toward the end of a two-hour test period the figures were 50 and 85 per cent respectively. Obviously the early social experience had some effect in making the chicks more socially inclined in the subsequent test situation.

After this part of the experiment all the chicks lived in flocks for six weeks, then were checked again in the test cage. Now there was no appreciable difference between those who had spent their first four weeks in isolation and those who had had social contacts during their first four weeks. Obviously, this early isolation had not ruined the birds socially for the rest of their lives. If it was a handicap, they overcame it.

The results of the experiment also showed that those who spent their first four weeks with a single companion did just as well in the test as did those who spent that four weeks with a whole flock. This is a bit analogous to the amount of instruction received. In this case a single companion was able to furnish enough social instruction [3].

Cooperation

Common Enemy / The preceding discussion of flocking dealt merely with getting together and doing things with no collective effort or apparent cooperation. However, such cooperation does occur at times against some common enemy. Robins versus cats furnish an everyday example, and if you hear frantic chirping from several robins, look for a cat nearby. If a cat gets a young robin, several adults will buzz the predator, although they seldom actually hit it. Starlings have been observed to cooperate against a hawk. Once, there were 25 of them in a loose flock when a marsh hawk flew up, and they closed ranks, veered to one side and, after the hawk had gained a little altitude, dived at it. The hawk had not been attacking them at the time but apparently they went after it on general principles [13]. Similarly, grackles have been observed to mob a perched Cooper's hawk, a barn owl and also a stuffed model of a great horned owl [11].

Sometimes several species combine against a common enemy. A group of 20 birds, including towhees, two species of wren, and titmice were observed scolding collectively and moving around in the brush about four feet above the ground. It was discovered that the object of their concern was the shed skin of a large rattlesnake that they evidently did not differentiate from the real thing. At any rate, it was a common enemy [2].

We find occasionally what looks like the equivalent of "sentries," a familiar instance being the blue jay screaming when some hostile creature is in the vicinity, thus warning some birds besides other jays. A species of stilt appears to serve as sentry for curlews, plovers and other shorebirds nesting in the Bear River Delta [14, p. 207]. Whether the sentry is actually posted for that purpose is problematical, and we cannot be sure to what extent he is deliberately warning the other birds. Perhaps his individual alarm at the predator merely is loud enough to be heard by the others, but it is helpful nevertheless and may even discourage the predator.

This mechanism whereby individuals that are not too congenial unite against a common enemy is not confined to birds. We have it ourselves. In the old days the Scottish clans used to fight each other until the British came across the border. Thereupon they united against this common enemy and after he was taken care of, they resumed fighting each other again.

Disliked Species / Cooperation is not always effected against an actual enemy but sometimes against a species that is merely disliked for some reason. The animosity of crows toward owls or hawks is a case in point. Owls do not eat young crows often enough to qualify as enemies, so perhaps the animosity comes from way back, buried somewhere in evolution. This tendency is convenient for bird watchers who are interested in seeing hawks or owls; if a large number of crows in one spot are heard, one can often go over and find an owl or hawk that they are tormenting.

Cooperation in Feeding / While birds often come to the same feeding place simultaneously, there are times when they actually help each other to some extent in the foraging process. Cormorants advance in a long line toward a school of fish, and individuals keep making short dives. Perhaps half of the birds are underwater at any one time, thus driving the fish ahead and limiting their dodging [4]. Similarly, brown pelicans form a crude arc, swim toward the shallow water beating their wings, then scoop up the fish that are beached. Scattered individual herring gulls cruise around looking for food, and if one finds a small amount of food, it eats silently. But if the supply is large, the gull gives the "food finding" call, which can be heard a long distance, and the others come. Sometimes the finder gives the cue by the way he flies, a figure eight in descending flight serving as a food indicator.

There was one case of three eagles who took turns in dragging a dead cormorant ashore since it was too heavy to be picked up, and when it was finally beached, the three of them shared the food. We cannot be sure that they deliberately rotated duties; it is conceivable that all three were interested in dragging the food ashore but could not all get hold of it at once: when one stopped, another automatically continued the process that it would have done anyway if it could [21, p. 119]. At least they did not fight over the food.

Preening / A cooperative manifestation in quite a different setting is mutual preening. Anyone who has watched a monkey cage has noticed a lot of this kind of behavior. In gregarious species of birds one individual often grooms another, especially on the head. It seems that the action is not merely a matter of removing dirt since it does not depend upon the amount of dirt present. It appears more like a social performance and presumably tends to reduce aggression and increase what might be called friendliness [27].

Helping / There are cases where one bird helps another with some activity in which the latter is engaged. This is more apt to occur in connection with feeding young. Sometimes parents are overburdened with the demands of their nestlings for food and a neighbor brings some food to fill the gap, literally as well as figuratively, or perhaps the neighbor brings some food anyway and the parents can relax slightly although they could handle the feeding chores themselves. Help is sometimes given in building nests and may extend even to incubating the eggs and brooding the young. It is not necessarily limited to helping one's own species, and song sparrows have been known to assist cardinals in this way, and robins and yellow warblers have helped each other. At least 130 species have been observed at this helpful kind of behavior [24].

The question arises as to just why some birds do it, since it is not a universal thing even within a species. Some of these helpers are birds hatched the previous season who have failed to secure a mate in the present season. Most birds pair off successfully, but for some reason there are leftovers, or bachelors and spinsters, as it were, in the bird population. Some of the normal seasonal urges, such as the tendency to feed young birds, may be present in such individuals even though they do not have families of their own, and they may find some outlet for this urge at a friend's nest. This type of thing is frequent at the human level. Many of us can recall a spinster aunt who was attentive to us in childhood. We cannot extrapolate to infancy, but presumably the tendency was even more pronounced then.

Again, there are cases where a pair of birds has more than one brood during the season. A bird from the first brood may become physically competent by the time the second brood arrives and may help out in feeding them. This is much like the older child that helps care for a younger brother or sister. In the case of the young bird we are not sure just what triggers this particular response. At that tender age the bird does not have the characteristic seasonal drive to feed young and there is no parental compulsion, but something in the social situation stimulates that kind of behavior. This tendency has been observed with bluebirds, barn swallows and some rails.

ADOPTION / When something happens to the parents of a young bird some other bird may assume the parental responsibilities in a way analogous to human adoption, or if an outside volunteer begins to feed the young quite consistently, the parents may quit and let him take over much as though they recognized a good thing. In one case a male Carolina wren served as foster parent for a family of house wrens: at the outset he fed the female house wren while she was incubating the eggs and then presently fed the young; finally, both house-wren parents left it all to him. A prothonotary warbler has been noted to help out with a yellow-warbler family [1, p. 168]. Similarly, a starling adopted a family of young robins, but when the young left the nest and perched in a tree 100 feet distant, the starling ignored their food calls. The relationship may have been rather casual anyway, but it is more likely that the sounds were so different from starling food calls that the bird did not recognize them as such and so did nothing foodwise [20].

SHARING NEST / Another variation of the tendency to cooperate occurs when the helpers not only share the work but also share the nest, a situation requiring considerable cooperation. Two cardinal families, two song-sparrow families and two pair of wood ducks have been known to do this.

FIGHTING

FIGHTING as a form of social behavior of birds is more conspicuous than cooperation and more dramatic, but it lacks the impact of a good dogfight and there is not apt to be as much injury to the participants. While birds may take a stuffed model apart, in a live combat the loser usually gets away before he is too severely cut up. To be sure, we have occasional fatalities, but they are infrequent.

Two situations frequently induce fighting. First, there is obvious conflict when both parties want to eat the same bit of food, and presumably there are times when this is a matter of survival, but the tendency to fight over food carries over into less tense situations, such as crowding around a well-stocked feeder. Even when there is plenty of food, birds often exhibit a rather blind tendency to get it any way and in a hurry. There are some indications that the amount of fighting depends upon the number of birds after the food at one time. With evening grosbeaks at a feeder, for example, when there were only two present there was little aggressiveness, but with more than five birds present there was always fighting [12]. The second common locus for fights is nesting territory. We have mentioned already how the male sets up his territory and defends it preparatory to getting a mate and building a nest. After the prospective mate arrives the territorial male has all the more reason to fight intruding males.

There are some instances, however, when it would appear that the fighting is done just for its own sake. In one instance two chickadees were fighting, with much attendant commotion, which attracted others, who came perhaps to watch but presently joined in. Sometimes as many as eight birds got into the act. The later ones apparently did not join because of food, which was how it all started, because they made no effort to get the food while they were there. Presumably the general excitement of the situation was enough to trigger a fighting response in them. Perhaps these particular birds were more belligerent anyway and more easily aroused. We shall see later that there are individual differences in personality among birds, and this group may have had more of the fighting personality [7]. An extension of this is seen in the gamecock, where selective breeding is sometimes used to ensure aggressiveness.

FRUSTRATION-AGGRESSION / A situation that sometimes induces aggressive behavior in people is the so-called frustration-aggression mechanism. A child wants to go outside but is not permitted to, so he smashes up some toys or furniture, taking out his frustration by aggressive behavior. There are a few cases resembling this mechanism in birds. A bluebird, for example, frustrated by a recording of a bluebird song and unable to find the rival, simply tore up its own nest as an outlet for the frustration [1, p. 124]. Similarly, a shrike punctured its own eggs. A cowbird may solicit preening by some other bird, as described earlier, but if its friend does not cooperate, then it turns around and attacks. A male cowbird in the course of an hour solicited preening from a red-winged blackbird 93 times with not too much success and in that period pecked the other bird three times, probably as an outlet for the frustration. With a stuffed dummy a cowbird displayed a preening invitation and after a few attempts attacked the dummy [23].

Peck Order / Fighting is almost inevitable in connection with establishing a peck order in a group of birds. In Chapter VI we described learning one's place in the hierarchy of dominance by means of encounters. Presently the peck order becomes fairly stable, as may be observed at a feeder. Young grackles who have not yet settled the problem when at a feeder hop or peck at each other, stick out their chests, turn their bills upward and stare. Meanwhile they do not eat and are thus wasting valuable time. The adult grackles, who have worked it out earlier and know who is number one and number two, arrive at the feeder and get right down to the business of eating. Number one eats first, then number two and so on. Hopefully there is enough food for all. At least no time is wasted in fighting [1, p. 117]. Basically this tendency to establish a peck order depends upon differences in aggressiveness between individuals, which will be considered more appropriately in Chapter X.

Social Facilitation

In the present context we should note again the way that an activity is enhanced by the presence of another bird engaging in the same activity. In Chapter III the principal manifestation of this social facilitation was discussed in connection with eating. A bird that had eaten to satiation ate additional food when a hungry bird was introduced and began to eat. The stimulus obviously was social in nature.

Social Relations with Outside Species

So far we have considered the social psychology of the bird in association primarily with others of its own species. It is conceivable, however, that birds of different species might find each other compatible and might even find the association profitable, as in seeking food together. Actually one does encounter feeding parties composed of several species. Chickadees often form the nucleus of the group, and in autumn and spring migrating warblers and vireos often join them and all move around as a group, the call notes of the chickadees tending to keep the group together. The warblers usually are a transient population and presently leave for their ultimate destination, but while they are in the vicinity, they act as if there was some social bond with the chickadees.

Again, in winter some of the permanent-resident birds join with chickadees in similar fashion. In Illinois a census made as to the composition of feeding parties found that practically all of them included chickadees, two-thirds of them downy woodpeckers and most of them titmice. Golden-crowned kinglets and white-breasted nuthatches were also quite frequently in the group [7]. It is interesting that although these species are isolationists with respect to breeding, they seem to be tolerant of the other species in the sense that they flock together and feed communally.

Some oceanic birds, including species of different size have been observed foraging together in mixed flocks, the smaller species living on "crumbs" dropped by the larger ones. This may not be actual cooperation and the crumbs may be accidental, but at least the small birds profit by the arrangement and the large ones do not prevent it.

A more extreme manifestation of association outside one's own species is the bird which spends considerable time with some entirely different animal. However, this is not as "broad-minded" or extremely social as it might seem. Usually the securing of food is basic to the relationship. We have mentioned already the cattle egret, which eats the insects flushed by the cattle; probably it has no attraction to the cattle as such. Similarly, a tropical bird resembling a cuckoo follows the cows around for the same reason. Some quantitative observations were made by counting the insects caught per minute with and without the cow as a "beater." In the dry season the birds caught half an insect per minute on their own and one and one-half when the cow was present. In the wet season the corresponding figures were 3.4 and 4.7. Similarly, the egret when following cattle obtained 1.25–1.5 as much food per unit time as when foraging alone and spent two thirds as much energy. The utility of the arrangement is obvious [21, p. 169].

The drongo (African species) follows elephants about. When

the elephants tear branches from a tree a lot of insects are dislodged and the birds fly in a manner similar to a flycatcher after the insects. Certain sandpipers ride the backs of hippopotami as they move along the shoreline, thus having a better view of the shoreline and edible aquatic creatures drifting past than they could get by working through the brush on the shore [22]. Another variation is a starlinglike bird in Africa that picks insects from the back of a rhinoceros, a service that helps both parties. Egrets have been observed to approach crocodiles and pick out bits of food that are stuck between the crocodile's teeth. Offhand this would seem a dangerous place to feed, but apparently it works out that the crocodile is not interested in eating the egret. There also are the honeyguides in Africa, which discover a bee's nest and manage to lead some mammal, usually a badger or a man, to the nest. After the nest is broken up, the honeyguides eat a lot of the wax.

One type of association of this sort apparently does not involve food at all. Some European starlings in cold weather were found in association with sheep, actually taking cover on the ground underneath the sheep. The observer thought it was the same starlings and the same group of sheep day after day [19]. This may not be a species characteristic, since these particular starlings may have blundered into the shelter, found it satisfactory and simply learned to use it regularly.

We are not sure about the origin of all this tendency for association. There have not been enough observations, except possibly for the cattle egret, to be certain that these behaviors occur in the species generation after generation and that the young do it without training. Obviously, some of these behaviors could be learned. Pigeon hawks, for example, followed a locomotive down the right of way and swooped on small birds that were flushed by the locomotive; presumably this was not a genetic tendency that had evolved because of its survival value, since such a development takes thousands of years and there have not been locomotives for that long.

Antisocial Behavior

Theft / Homo sapiens has no monopoly on antisocial behavior. The most obvious case among birds is what we would call larceny, robins frequently being victims. English sparrows were observed to take six worms from a robin, one after the other. A starling stole four worms from a robin in five minutes.

More dramatic cases occur in the air. An eagle dives at an osprey flying with a fish in its talons, and the osprey drops the fish, which the eagle retrieves—frequently before it hits the ground or the water. A jaeger performs an almost identical robbery with terns. When a red-tailed hawk approached a perched peregrine falcon holding a pigeon, the peregrine flew; however, the hawk flew under the falcon, and the latter dropped the pigeon, which the hawk followed down. The falcon screamed but otherwise ignored the theft. This incident happened in a region where the rodents that formed the hawk's usual diet were scarce, and a pigeon was a fair substitute [5].

Some instances of theft occur on the water. Some species of ducks, such as baldpates, normally dabble for vegetation in shallow water, while other ducks, such as redheads, dive for their food. In a winter location where appropriate vegetation was scarce near the surface, baldpates were observed to steal it quite regularly from the redheads who brought it up from the depths. In another place a baldpate and a gadwall followed a coot, and when the latter surfaced with some pondweed the other two birds pounced on him.

Some robbery also is done along the shore. Laughing gulls have been noted stealing from pelicans—sometimes taking the food directly from their pouches. Sanderlings give it a little different twist in stealing from a turnstone; when the latter turns over stones to expose food, the sanderlings rush in and seize it before the turnstone can get it himself. One sanderling doing this was observed to drive other sanderlings away, apparently keeping a good thing to himself.

In one case involving more violence, a skua attacked a gannet, seized it by the wing until it crashed and then held it down until it disgorged some food, which the skua then ate.

Robbery directed at eggs or young in the nest is practiced by wrens, grackles, crows, jays and some gulls. Generally the egg or the nestling is taken as food, but sometimes a bird merely injures the eggs without eating them. The wren punches holes in them, while others push the egg out of a nest rather than puncturing it—which comes pretty close to vandalism. Of course, if the nest in question is near the bird's own nest, it might be part of the tendency to defend one's territory. Such attacks that reduce the population of another species and presumably make more food available for the offender and his species might be a genetic tendency. Again, the attacks may be just part of a belligerent personality.

In comparison with the human species, victims of theft such as just described do not appear very resentful of the situation. The robins were much larger than the sparrows that stole the worms from them, but the robins made no preventive or retaliatory effort and merely located other worms. Robins and other thrushes are not very belligerent anyway, but some of the other species that are more belligerent did not appear very disturbed by losing the food. In our human species, of course, theft is regarded as "wrong," but birds apparently do not have such a concept and accept larceny as a matter of course. Since there is nothing analogous to punishment, the only deterent to the crime would be if the victim struck back or threatened the prospective thief as he approached.

Parasites / One other type of antisocial behavior may be noted: parasitism in connection with the incubation of eggs and feeding of young. The most notorious offender hereabouts is the cowbird, but some species of cuckoo do it and even a few species of ducks, as will be discussed.

Cowbirds never build a nest, but the female lays her eggs (usually one or two) in the nest of some other species and the parents of the latter incubate the eggs and take care of the young. The cowbird is fairly successful at timing the parasitism and has been observed to "case" a warbler's nest, watching the nest building and occasionally going up and looking into the nest. The cowbird even removed one or two eggs from the warbler's nest, but it did not molest nests that it was not going to use.

Although a cowbird has been known to invade a brown thrasher's nest, the parasite generally selects some smaller species as victim, an effective arrangement from the cowbird's standpoint because then the cowbird nestling will be the biggest one in the nest, with the largest mouth and the longest neck and thus will get most of the food. Sometimes the young of the parasite species is big and strong enough to do physical damage to the other nestlings. Young birds of a species of cuckoo in Europe have a little hook on the tip of the bill which is used to kill the fellow nestlings. As the cuckoos get older, the hook drops off.

Parasitism may be pretty serious from the standpoint of bird population. The Kirtland warbler, for instance, which nests in a very limited area in Michigan, so that accurate observation is possible, had a count made of eggs lost or destroyed by parasitism plus the mortality of nestlings that, for some reason, did not mature to the point of leaving the nest on their own. The total of these two losses was 43 per cent of what would have been the contribution to the next generation of warblers had there been no parasites [18]. In another project cowbirds were trapped and killed in one area in comparison with an area where they were not controlled. In the first area three-fourths of the Kirtland nests were successful in the sense that the young survived to leave the nest, while in the latter only one-fourth lived.

After the parasite egg is hatched, the foster parent apparently does not discriminate and acts as if the nestling were its own. After all, the stimulus of a wide open mouth is just a wide open mouth and touches off the instinctive drive to put something in it. As the nestling develops, the foster parent evidently becomes accustomed to the intruder and carries on. Frequently one will see a small adult bird feeding a young cowbird that actually is larger than itself. The writer once saw a young cowbird not very long out of the nest in a trap, and a chipping sparrow, evidently the foster parent, came up and fed the cowbird through the wire of the trap. Evidently the urge to feed this pseudo-offspring was quite strong. Records show that 206 species of birds have been parasitized, although many of them are not often hosts [30].

In some regions a startling proportion of the nests of a given species are parasitized. In an area along the roadsides in Nebraska, 54 per cent of the red-wing nests that were found had been parasitized, as had 53 per cent of the dickcissel nests and 16 per cent of the meadowlark nests. No parasitism was found at all in mourning-dove nests, but then the mourning dove is two or three times as large as the cowbird [16].

Cowbirds, as indicated above, always parasitize, whereas some species do so only occasionally. Although ducks generally operate their own nests, there are 21 species that on occasion parasitize. Redhead ducks and ruddy ducks are especially prone to do so, but individuals within the species differ, and something like 5 to 10 per cent of the redhead ducks never parasitize at all as far as could be observed, while others do it some of the time.

There also are "dump" nests, and 13 different females have been known to lay eggs in the same nest—just who took over from there on is not clear. Probably the tendency to "dump" would not be very effective biologically [29].

The victim of parasitism does not always ignore it. As indicated above, when matters reach the stage of a big open mouth, then the usual tendency prevails, but at the egg stage, it may be a different story. The bird may be able to recognize a foreign egg, in which case three types of behavior are used in meeting the situation: first, throwing the foreign egg out of the nest or even burying it; second, deserting the nest; third, building a new floor in the nest right over the old and thus covering up the egg. Yellow warblers have been observed to follow the third alternative, and furthermore, if the second nest floor was parasitized, to build still another nest on top of the second. The record is a six-story nest built in this fashion, in which there were 11 cowbird eggs, but the warbler persisted in inactivating all of them [6].

The house wren is a natural egg wrecker, punching holes in eggs or pushing them out of the nest, an advantageous tendency if a cowbird egg is laid in the wren's nest. There is a marked difference in the size of the eggs, which perhaps gives the wren its clue. However, if a cowbird nestling is introduced experimentally into the wren's nest, it is accepted. As suggested above, the egg stage appears to be the time when the victim is able to do something about the parasitism.

Thus, species respond differently to parasitism if they respond at all. It has been suggested that parasitism came along rather late in the course of evolution and that the victim species have not had time to evolve a uniformly satisfactory method of coping with it. Perhaps after many generations such uniformity will appear [1, p. 130].

If birds did uniformly throw out every cowbird egg, the problem would disappear, as would cowbirds unless they in turn adopted some countermeasure. A few of them might build their own nests (mutation), and the only surviving cowbirds would manifest this same tendency; presently the species would nest normally and parasitism would disappear.

Birds of some species seem to recognize the cowbird as an enemy or at least as undesirable. Whether they are actually aware of what the cowbird is planning to do is problematical. But at least the victim may show aggressive behavior toward the parasite in advance of any egg laying. A redstart, for example, even before its nest was built, threatened a cowbird by posture or by snapping its bill. The redstart was much smaller, but if a cowbird approached the nest, the redstart landed on its back and pecked at its head. Sometimes under these conditions the cowbird gave up and left [10]. Song sparrows do much the same thing, as do robins. However, ovenbirds and Kirtland warblers apparently do not recognize the cowbird as an enemy and have never been observed to attack it.

The cowbird on its part may adopt what looks like countermeasures to break up the hostile attitude, to "soften up" the potential host, as it were. The countermeasure is the invitation to preening mentioned elsewhere. The cowbird lowers its head and fluffs the feathers at the back of its neck where the host might preen. (Some writers have used the word "appeasement" to describe this and point out that it involves exposing the vulnerable area where a blow might injure the base of the skull and the brain tissue underneath, but this may be an overstatement.) Mutual preening is actively indulged in when the situation is congenial rather than belligerent, so there might be at least some kind of an effort on the part of the cowbird to minimize belligerence.

This preening invitation has been studied with captive birds. Ten cowbirds were placed in a cage and then a bird of another species was introduced, and the preening displays were counted. With a female red-wing, the ten cowbirds in one hour did 265 of these preening displays [23], so the cowbirds evidently were taking the situation seriously. On the other hand, the host was seldom impressed enough to respond favorably to these invitations, so we cannot tell whether they were effective in reducing hostility and increasing the probability of the victim's eventually accepting the eggs in the nest. It looks like a good try anyway.

Social behavior such as we have been discussing involves mutual response between birds. This response communicates information, some of the methods of which have been implicit in our discussion. In the next chapter we shall consider in more detail these means of communication used by birds.

CHAPTER VIII

How Birds Communicate

Social life for birds, or any other animals, for that matter, is meaningless without methods of communication. The other bird is something more than a tree or rock or bit of food; it is a social stimulus that talks back. If we listen to a group of birds, it certainly sounds as if some communication is taking place, although it is unintelligible to us. If we observe closely, we may detect a considerable variety of sounds. In fact, birds are better off than many other animals in this respect. Dogs and cats have very limited vocabularies; fish grunt now and then; frogs trill; crickets chirp—but birds express alarm, distress and aggressiveness, call a group together, announce a source of food and make appropriate vocal response to a member of the opposite sex.

We are most aware of birds' communication by way of song, especially in the early morning, but that is only part of it. Quite a bit is handled by posture or gesture. Some species, woodpeckers and grouse, for instance, make communicatory sounds that are not vocal at all. Most birds have various call notes that are simpler than a song but still transmit information to the other birds.

Posture

Aggressiveness / We shall begin with postures or gestures. The most obvious of these are made in connection with aggressive behavior, and there is a lot of contention in a bird's life. Fortunately, many of the conflicts can be resolved by mere posture since too much actual fighting might be disadvantageous from the survival standpoint.

A common aggressive pose is the holding of the head forward with the bill lowered, a logical enough pose, as it might be the initial stages of an attack. Sometimes the bird actually moves forward slightly in the process but not far enough for contact, and sometimes in addition the wings are spread and the feathers fluffed, which may suggest action or perhaps make the bird look a bit larger. Some species, including pectoral sandpipers and grackles, carry the head straight up for aggressiveness rather than down, while the giant petrel uses both up and down. When his aggressiveness is directed at a single adversary, he lowers the head, but when he is confronting several, he holds the head high. The reason for this is not clear. We may note that even the direction in which the bird faces is of some importance in this kind of communication. Aggressive birds generally face each other, but when they are engaged in pair formation they are more apt to move parallel to one another.

Birds often display aggressively any conspicuous feature of plumage. The red-wing blackbird spreads his wings to show the red epaulets; the mockingbird cocks his tail vertically and fans it so as to show the white of the tail feathers (he does this toward a predator such as a cat or squirrel); the shrike flashes the white on his wings; the white-breasted nuthatch shows the white wing and tail markings by spreading wings and tail.

Some aggressive displays are more unusual. The prairie chickens stomp and boom; the buff-breasted sandpiper holds a single wing straight up; the fulmar spits an oily substance on an opponent—apparently if voice and posture are inadequate, the spit does it. Chickadees sometimes put on a "snake display," plunging forward and hissing, thus reminding us that birds evolved from reptilian ancestors. The chickadee makes this display against a predator such as a wren looking into the hole in which the chickadee is nesting.

The rose-breasted grosbeak combines positive and negative responses in aggressiveness. When a squirrel is robbing the nest, the bird moves toward it and away from it alternately, sometimes holding its feathers in sleek fashion, sometimes ruffing them [3].

Aggressive displays may be made at a rather early age. White-crowned sparrows have been known to display at nine days of age—and they are not fully feathered until ten days old.

We find different degrees of aggressive response as the situation gets more intense. A house finch may merely fly in and perch beside an opponent, who then perhaps leaves. If this does not happen, the finch gives a head-forward display with its wings held in normal position; the next step is to elevate the wings slightly and crouch. The bird does not go through the entire sequence unless necessary. Similarly, the white-eye leans forward, opens the bill, droops the wing and stares at the opponent. At the next level, it flutters the wings and gives some kind of a sound; at the third stage, it starts pecking.

There are cases where the aggression may be blocked and the drive takes some other outlet. Gulls' pulling up grass is a case in point.

APPEASEMENT / Appeasement, the converse of aggressive behavior, is sometimes found among birds. There may be hostility but they want to get along with the hostile party. One way to do this is to invite mutual preening, which is a common practice between birds that are friendly. Cowbirds were discussed earlier [22]. The kittiwake appeases by concealing its beak. When kittiwakes fight, the usual procedure is to attack the other party's beak. In one case, a bird attacking a model made 98 per cent of its passes at the beak. Therefore, an intruder near a nest on a small ledge squats down and hides its beak, which tends to prolong its stay since it is less apt to provoke an attack when there is no standard item to attack. Even young kittiwakes demonstrate this behavior when they are fighting in the nest. One tucks its beak under its breast presumably to avoid a fight [6].

COURTSHIP / Another situation that is implemented by gestures is courtship. If the gestures are specific enough, the female song sparrow may confine her interest to other song sparrows rather than to vesper sparrows, for example, thus avoiding possible hybridizing, which is not too desirable genetically. This same principle keeps two species of grackles on the Gulf Coast separate [21]. Species differ as to the actual gestures used in the process, which include various motions of the head or tail, or display of conspicuous plumage. We shall discuss them in more detail in the next chapter.

FOOD / Occasionally, there are some gestures in connection with food, although vocal communication is more common in this situation. Herring gulls have scouts that go around looking for food and when they discover it may do a sort of figure eight in their descending flight, which the other birds recognize. Young birds beg for food with a rapid flutter of their wings and an abbreviated wing beat. Of course, they use vocal sounds along with this.

Nonvocal Sounds

Tapping / Some bird communication takes place by way of sounds that are not vocal. The common instance in the woods is furnished by the woodpeckers, which tap on dead trees in a rapid rhythm, the volume of the sound depending somewhat on the size of the bird and the resonant characteristics of the tree. Downy woodpeckers drum 16 times per second and hairy woodpeckers 25. Some of the activity is merely pecking holes for nesting or for shelter, but some of it is actually signaling. The male red-bellied woodpecker taps at a prospective nest site; then the female comes along and joins the tapping apparently to indicate approval of the site—at least, that is where they drill the hole and raise the family. Again, the male spends the night in the cavity and in the morning starts tapping on the inside, whereupon the female comes along and taps on the outside for some reason. Pileated woodpeckers do much the same thing when selecting a nest site. The mutual tapping when they agree upon the location is a rapid roll, lasting about one second. Prior to that, the male in advertising his territory and attracting a female gives rolls of about three seconds' duration and at intervals of about 40 to 60 seconds [11]. The pileated woodpecker also gives a sharp rap against almost any surface when he is nervous or excited. Whether he is transmitting information or merely finding an outlet for his excitement is not known. Around residential districts, woodpeckers may tap on a tin roof or metal stovepipe as a signal. Flickers, too, are frequent offenders.

The bill is used for sounds other than tapping. Some species click the mandibles together—storks rattle them like castanets and can be heard for half a mile, and the road runner does much the same thing. The male black-crowned night heron on the breeding grounds stands over a crude nest platform, holds a stick in his bill and snaps his bill on it loudly, moving his head up and down. It is easy to infer what he is trying to communicate and presumably the female gets the point.

WING SOUNDS / Some birds in flight produce audible sounds with their wings, mourning doves being perhaps the most familiar. Among the ducks, the goldeneye gives a sort of whistling sound and in fact is sometimes called the whistler. Some of these sounds may be merely by-products of actual flight, while others, such as the sound of the wings on takeoff, may constitute signals of some sort. The male goldeneye's wing sounds are louder than those of the female, which may have some significance in connection with territory or attracting the opposite sex. Some young nestlings begin to beg when they hear the wings of the parent bird approaching the nest and get their mouths open and ready. The chimney swift actually snaps its wings together five or six times to repel an intruder. There also are wing sounds as part of the courting display. The woodcock, for example, flies up about 70 feet and then dives rapidly with a sort of winnowing sound made by the wing feathers, which evidently is part of the technique for arousing interest of the female. In the deep woods, one can hear a grouse drumming in dramatic fashion. The beat is around 40 cycles per second, and the sound is made entirely by the wings in the air and they do not hit anything. This again is for the benefit of the female.

CALL NOTES

MANY birds communicate by means of call notes, sounds made by the vocal apparatus but briefer and simpler than the usual songs. We do not notice them so much, but it is generally agreed that they are more important than the songs in the day-to-day communication between birds [9]. Birds have no true speech like us in the way of nouns, verbs, etc., and if we had to classify their calls, they would probably be exclamations or interjections in our sense, since they usually indicate some emotional state, just as a baby's cry does when he is in distress or hungry or in need of something. These calls are significant to other members of the species and touch off different responses in different situations, as well as helping individuals recognize each other. The sounds may, on occasion, be significant to other species, as the blue jay in the neighborhood serves as somewhat of a sentinel for all the residents and screams at cats or other predators. We may now look at some of the functions of these call notes in more detail.

Alarm / Most birds have alarm notes in their repertoire. Life is hazardous, with predators or other enemies in the offing, and if a bird spies such enemy, it is common practice to notify the other birds. These others react to the alarm notes all right. For instance, a flock of white-eyes (small New Zealand birds) were observed at a feeder, and when one gave the alarm note at the sight of a cat, all the birds flew away on cue.

The operation of these alarm notes can be seen clearly when they are recorded on tape and played back to the birds. Herring gulls fled from the feeding dumps when the appropriate alarm note was played, and starlings responded to their alarm note by leaving the roost temporarily. Whether the alarm note specifies the nature of the danger and where to go is uncertain, but at any rate something happens that usually is advantageous for the listeners. A domestic hen gave harsh screams at the sight of a hawk but merely cackled when a dog or man appeared, which seems like designation of the danger, but it is possible that the latter response was not an actual alarm note. A western species of partridge used three different kinds of alarm notes that were qualitatively different even to humans: (1) a ground alarm—*whitoo;* (2) an alarm when a hawk appears—*kerrr;* (3) caution when a hawk continues to soar overhead but presumably is not in the process of attack—a low-pitched undulating *kwerrr* [23]. This last case suggests some differentiation in the calls and the transmitting of more information than mere alarm. Herring gulls do not do so well in this respect. An observer was sitting in a blind near a gull colony when a parent bird was alarmed by an inadvertent movement of the observer, gave the alarm call and walked away. The young did not follow the adult as intended but actually went right into the blind. Obviously, the directions to the young were inadequate, but at least the young moved. Under ordinary circumstances almost any movement would be helpful because blinds are seldom encountered by birds in the wild [25, p. 55]. Occasionally, we find a bird that sees a predator and gives alarm notes all by himself when no other birds are present. This is not a social stimulus in the usual sense in that he is not trying to communicate his alarm to other birds. It is much like the way we say "ouch" if we hurt ourselves when nobody else is around.

The different species have their own alarm notes, of course, but they may learn to recognize the alarm notes of other species, such as the blue jay. In another instance, the alarm notes of crows in France were recorded and then these records were played to some crows in Pennsylvania in the winter. The latter showed no response to the notes at all. One might facetiously say that they did not understand French. However, the next summer the experimenter was repeating the procedure in order to demonstrate to a visitor how his crows did not respond to the French alarm notes. To his surprise (and embarrassment) the crows actually scattered in alarm. Presently, it developed that he was dealing with a different population. Those birds summering in Pennsylvania had wintered in Florida, where they had mixed in with fish crows, whose calls are quite similar to those of the French variety, so naturally they responded to the recorded French calls. However, the birds wintering in Pennsylvania that were subjected to the first playback went north in the summer and never encountered fish crows, which explains their lack of interest in the recordings [8].

Distress / Some birdcalls indicate distress rather than just alarm. Of course the birds may be frightened also, but there seems to be some differentiation. These distress calls can be evoked from a bird held in the hand or in the grip of some enemy or predator. Young birds will frequently give such calls if they are cold. Other birds, hearing the distress calls, react in one of two ways. First, they may come to investigate, presumably out of curiosity or possibly in order to help the bird in distress. They may even go through a semblance of attack upon whatever is molesting the bird. Every bird bander has experienced this. Bird watchers make a squeak on the back of the hand which resembles a distress call and many birds pop out of the underbrush for a closer look. The writer has even had a barred owl come out to see what the fuss was all about. Possibly it was hungry at the time. The second response to the distress calls is to fly away from the source in an apparent effort to avoid trouble themselves. When recorded distress calls are played, blackbirds sometimes leave the roost—a procedure that has been used in an effort to control the nuisance, as was discussed in more detail elsewhere. What usually happens is that the sound merely drives them to some other neighborhood nearby.

Assembly Call / Some species have an assembly or rallying call, which sometimes unites them against a common enemy, such as crows assembling to pester an owl or hawk. If we play recordings of assembly calls, many birds appear from nowhere. At other times, the call serves to keep the group together. For example, bobwhites in a covey call back and forth and this serves to keep the family intact. The same thing happens with some species of partridge. When wood warblers, sparrows and thrushes are migrating at night, these assembly notes may help keep the group together so that they all reach about the same destination. While the assembly call keeps the birds in the vicinity, it does not necessarily jam them too close together. If they were all shoulder to shoulder, they might have difficulty in finding enough food. They need to spread out a little but still remain fairly near. Ruby-crowned kinglets have been observed to operate in this way.

Food Call / Food calls are used in two ways: to announce the presence of food or to yell for it. With reference to the first, a gull will scout for food and if it finds some, at least more than it needs for its own use, it gives a three-syllable cry that can be heard for three miles. Domestic hens have a food call different from the warning calls or the invitation to come and brood. On the other hand, young birds call for food. Robins give a single peep at first and a two-syllable call a little later, after they have left the nest officially or have gotten out of it prematurely. Some of these food calls may be very insistent—a parent redstart returning to the nest with food was waylaid by a young cowbird calling from a red-eyed vireo's nest and the cowbird got the food [1, p. 152].

Sex and Nesting / Special notes are uttered by some birds during nest building. We do not hear all of them because they are soft, appropriately enough. The female song sparrow has some call notes that the male does not have and uses them in the appropriate situation. Goldfinches have a special warbling note that they use during nest building and incubation.

RECOGNITION / Call notes are often used in recognizing individual birds. The Adélie penguin in a big rookery recognizes its mate by the voice when the mate returns after an absence of months. Young birds will respond selectively to the parent's voice that has been recorded on tape and distinguish it from the voices of other parent birds [19, p. 22]. Thus it is evident that call notes play a big role in influencing bird behavior.

SONG FUNCTION

WE now come to communication by way of song as contrasted with call notes. This aspect is more significant and interesting to people but not necessarily so to the birds. Nevertheless singing generally has some utility, and we may interpret this by observing what is going on at the time.

TERRITORY / Probably the most conspicuous manifestation of song takes place when the male is setting up territory prior to nesting. Most of the vigorous outbursts that we hear on spring mornings serve this general purpose, which is usually the initial phase of the nesting cycle. The male selects a place in the appropriate habitat for the species and essentially stakes a claim, then announces this fact to the world—and especially to any rivals who might want the same territory. Sometimes this is called an advertising song.

Birds may sing prior to the actual establishment of territory. We noted earlier how glandular development is part of the story and it may trigger the migration; it may also trigger some song. Many birds begin singing about as soon as they start north, and we often hear many individual birds that are not going to nest in our region but are merely singing as they pass through, as is especially the case with some warblers. However, the majority wait until they reach the nesting area. The thrushes are particularly conservative in this respect, and although we see numerous hermit thrushes migrating through, we never hear them sing.

The territorial singing is done from a perch, usually a conspicuous one, such as a treetop, the top of a bush, a fence post or even a chimney. This not only helps advertise the presence of the bird visually as well as vocally, but also gives him a good view of the territory so he can spot an intruder and attack if necessary.

Species differ in the extent to which they sing in this situation. Some do it almost incessantly. The brilliantly colored birds get considerable advertising from their appearance, but the drab ones need more vocal advertising. It is a bit like magazine advertisements with good pictures, which do not need as much text. The extent of singing may vary also with population pressure. A British chaffinch has a song that is simpler and less variable than that of its opposite number on the Continent. In the former case, the population is less dense and there is not as much competition for space, so territorial proclamations are less important [24]. Another variable is the deep forest, where birds may not be able to find a visually conspicuous perch and have to rely more on song. Many of these deep-forest birds are rated as "good singers."

If several male birds are in the same general area but all on their individual territories, there may be some advantage when they all sing at once. This makes the whole area conspicuous and the increased volume may stop passing females more readily than would be the case if only one bird was singing, thus increasing the marital chances for most of these males. Hopefully, there will be enough females to go around.

Mating / The second function of song is to attract a mate. We cannot tell for certain whether the same song serves both functions as we do not understand the words, but at least both functions are involved in the same over-all performance. If the song is successful on both counts, the female joins the male and they go about the business of building a nest and raising a family.

There are a number of indications of the connection of song with getting a mate. One is that the song decreases after the mate is secured, since it is no longer necessary. This has been noted especially in warblers and finches. A particular flycatcher reduced its song from 3620 to 1000 per day after the arrival of the female [10]. A snow bunting stopped singing completely under these circumstances.

A bit of negative evidence is that in some species the female may desert the male if he does not sing vigorously enough. In a species of warbler, the female does just this if the male does not sing strenuously at intruders. On the other hand, the singing may shift to quiet little efforts while the pair is prospecting in the territory for a good nest site. Cardinals do this with "almost inaudible trills" [13].

A song that attracts a mate serves another purpose in that it brings a mate of the right species. We noted elsewhere how postures also help in this same respect. If two species look quite similar but have different songs, the female still is able to select the proper species. This selection extends even to two races of the same species. An instance of dialects, which we shall discuss more fully in a later section, is the alder flycatcher, which has two races, or subspecies, with two different songs. If we play a recording of one, the other pays little attention. Why interbreeding is undesirable is not clear, but in any case, the song does facilitate breeding with one's own subspecies.

IDENTIFICATION / Song has further utility in identifying the individual bird. Human experts on song can recognize several individual birds of the same species in an area. Probably the birds themselves can do much better. Adélie penguin parents and chicks recognize each other by sound [18]. When we study recordings we find plenty of differences between individual songs. Recorded songs of 70 birds of one species of junco (Mexican) were analyzed and no two were identical [15]. Presumably birds can recognize a rival or a mate in this way. When a pair of birds mates one year, gets separated during migration and then returns to the original area the next year, instances have been reported where the female presumably recognized her former "husband" by the song. Again, if several males on adjacent territories recognize each other's song, they may establish a way of life in which they do not resent this singing because it is not a threat, but they do recognize a foreigner as such and attack.

FEMALE SONG / The preceding discussion implies that most singing is done by the male birds, but occasionally a female will do a little on her own account. This is fairly common with cardinals, rose-breasted grosbeaks, purple finches and gray-cheeked thrushes; it occurs less frequently with the female summer tanager, indigo bunting, towhee, white-crowned sparrow and grasshopper sparrow. The female mockingbird does a sort of territorial song in the nonbreeding season, and the female wood thrush sings a little while incubating. We noted earlier how some female birds have their individual call notes during the nesting period. On the whole, however, the males have a monopoly on singing.

DUET / Occasionally the two sexes sing together. To cite a single instance, the male ovenbird gets practically through his song and then the female joins in and they end together. Apparently, this occurs only when the birds are paired and is part of the mating process. Several species of owls are reputed to sing duets.

MISCELLANEOUS FUNCTIONS / Singing occurs in some other situations where we cannot always be clear as to its function, one being when incubation is in progress. We have already mentioned how the female may sing softly while sitting on the eggs, which may be an invitation to the male to take his turn. The male also sings while the family is in the nest but not the loud territorial song. He may continue to sing after a fashion when the young are being fed out of the nest, as is the case with wrens, wood warblers and some finches.

Some observers report what they call emotional songs, which have no obvious function but perhaps are just emotional outlets. We do some of that ourselves—the close harmony in the shower at the gym. Five male grassquits (Southern birds) were observed in the same small bush, all singing together during nesting season. Obviously, they were not trying to keep the other birds away from their territory because they were all together. It may have been just some surplus emotion.

We occasionally find some singing during actual fighting. Wrens and some other birds give a sort of vocal challenge as they start to fight, and after bits of song they scuffle in the air. Dippers often fight on the water and with their wings beat each other's heads below the surface. In one instance, every time a bird was submerged in this way it came up singing. Maybe this is like the growling and snarling of some mammals when they fight [2, p. 129].

Flight Song / Some species do their singing primarily in flight. Bobolinks are the everyday case, and horned larks do likewise high in the air. Some birds, however, sing from a perch and have a separate flight song. This is true for the goldfinch and the ovenbird. Still others—some blackbirds and wrens—may do snatches of their regular song when flying.

Time of Day / Morning song is the most conspicuous—perhaps because it wakes us up—but song continues off and on during the day. The red-eyed vireo sings all day long, and an indefatigable observer counted 22,197 songs in one day from one bird. At twilight there may be some more of the morning song. Robin songs are especially noticeable just before dark. With some species, the evening song is different from the morning song, as is true of the Acadian flycatcher. Some birds even continue singing after dark, such as the mockingbird, chat, field sparrow and marsh wren. While singing usually is confined to the spring and the breeding season, there is some at other times of the year. It has been suggested that in winter some species appear to be defending a food territory in contrast to a nesting territory.

Mimicry / A few species of birds have songs which in part imitate those of other species. The mockingbird is well named. A member of this species was observed to imitate 55 other species of birds within an hour. Others that do a fair amount of mimicry are the thrasher and the catbird. Starlings even do a little and have been known to imitate bobwhites, pewees and meadowlarks. The experts do not agree on the function of this mimicry or why it should have survival value. Certainly the birds do not always do it at an appropriate time. A mockingbird, for example, gives the call of a nocturnal bird at noon or the call of a cuckoo at a season when the cuckoos have already stopped singing. A parrot's making the same remark whenever a certain person appears could be merely a conditioned response and the appropriateness of the remark is generally irrelevant.

Character of Song

In recent years, we have been able to study birdsongs in considerable detail thanks to tape recorders. The initial efforts along this line were rather clumsy and involved a truckload of heavy batteries. Now, with the advent of transistors, fairly light equipment is available. With a recording unit over his shoulder and a parabolic microphone in one hand, the expert can walk most any place comfortably and make his recordings.

There are also devices to convert the sound track into a graphic record (spectrogram) that gives time on one axis and the frequency of the sound vibration on the other axis. It is possible in this way to detect differences in song in much more detail than can be done by ear. Also, the record can be played back at one-half or one-quarter or one-eighth the normal speed, which facilitates certain kinds of analysis. Much of this work is too complicated for discussion here, but we may at least indicate some of the variables involved. Such analysis is not intended to detract from the pleasure of listening to birdsongs, which is as far as most people want to go anyway.

Variables in Song Character / Birdsongs may be analyzed in terms of several variables, one of which is pitch, which we mentioned in connection with our discussion of hearing and noted that a horned owl hoots at around 150 cycles per second. The blackpoll warbler, on the other hand, sings at about 8900 cycles. The average pitch for about 60 songbirds was around 4,280 cycles—just above the top note of the piano. There is an apparent relation of pitch to habitat. Nine species of wood warblers that sing from medium to high perches in the trees average about 6600 cycles, while seven species that forage and sing at lower levels average around 4000 cycles. The reason for this is not clear [7]. Some birds do their whole song all on one pitch. In other species there is marked change in pitch during the song; it may go up and up to the end (prairie warbler) or slur down and then up (wood pewee).

Another variable is loudness, which depends somewhat on the size of the bird. The American bittern is rather large and can be heard for up to three miles. The call of the large pileated woodpecker carries a mile and a half. The cuckoo can be heard for better than one mile [2, p. 33]. The smaller songbirds cannot approach this performance. Another loudness factor is that when a bird is singing to the female during courtship, the song naturally is more quiet and carries only a short distance, although there may be changes in loudness during the song. The ovenbird gives a characteristic crescendo.

Songs also differ greatly in quality, and a variety of descriptive adjectives are used by ornithologists as well as poets—whistling note of robin, raucous quacking of duck, plaintive call of white-throated sparrow, wiry note of Blackburnian warbler, buzz of grasshopper sparrow, trill of house wren.

Another variable is the temporal pattern, which may consist of long slow notes or short rapid notes. The speed may change—start slowly and end rapidly, as with the field sparrow—and there may be various combinations of long and short notes that approach poetic meter. The bay-breasted warbler makes a good attempt at trochaic hexameter except that he does not always stop at six measures.

The foregoing variables may occur in numerous combinations that make for a great variety of songs. The result is often distinctive enough so that one can recognize the species on hearing it, and some ornithologists making a bird census of an area actually rely more on their ears than their eyes.

Nevertheless, the sound spectrogram reveals a lot that the ear cannot catch. For instance, we *hear* the chipping sparrow give a series of rapid notes all on one pitch, but actually each note is slurred over about an octave—and this happens in one hundredth of a second. We miss this entirely but somehow it makes the notes sound dull. The junco's song is somewhat similar but the slurs are not so great nor so fast and the notes sound more musical [5].

Again, the spectrogram shows that a wood thrush in part of his song gives two notes simultaneously—sort of a chord. There are notes steady in pitch accompanied by lower notes rapidly slurred in pitch. We miss this accomplishment entirely when we merely listen.

Repertoire / Analysis of recordings enables us to determine the repertoire of an individual bird. In some cases the bird has just a single song type or pattern. This does not mean that all the other members of his species sing that same song, but at least each member is limited to his one song. This is the situation with the least flycatcher, grasshopper sparrow, ovenbird, junco and chipping sparrow, to mention a few.

Some individual birds however may have from two to seven

demonstrable types of song, as is typical of the phoebe, pewee, titmouse, field sparrow and redstart. Still other individuals, including towhee, song sparrow, wood thrush and Carolina wren, have a repertoire of eight or more.

We also may consider repertoire with reference to species rather than individual. While the individual junco has a single song, we find over 20 different junco songs if we get recordings from enough birds. The same thing is true for chipping sparrows and yellowthroats (warblers). In other cases the individual may have more than one song, but there is still more variation between members of the species [5].

Dialect / People in different regions of the country may speak different dialects, although Homo sapiens is one species. Similarly, birds of the same species in different areas have different dialects. We have already mentioned the alder flycatcher which apparently has two races, or subspecies. In New York state, this species sings a song that may be paraphrased *wee-bee-o*. In Ohio, on the other hand, the song sounds like *fitz-bew*. Birds in the two groups look almost identical but the song keeps them straight. If we play an Ohio song to a New Yorker at the nesting season, he does not come out to fight the way he does if we play him a New York song. Similarly, as mentioned earlier, French herring gulls ignore calls of the American herring gulls although the birds are otherwise very similar [8]. Song sparrows have geographic variations in their songs. On the Connecticut coast and in southeastern New York, they have a single long introductory note before the twittering part of the song. In central and western New York, they give two long introductory notes [20]. Towhees in Florida can be distinguished from the northern variety of the same species by song. A South Sea Island warbler has a beautiful song on some islands and an unmusical ditty on other islands. The value of these variations is not particularly clear but apparently the subspecies breed true and the song is what facilitates this breeding true.

Variation with Situation / The character of the bird's song or even the presence or absence of it may depend upon the situation at the time. The meadowlark changes his song as a person approaches the nest. Normally, there are four notes in the song, but when a person gets close, the song is shortened to two notes. In the early morning, the amount of light determines when the bird starts singing, as can be demonstrated by measuring the light with an appropriate meter and noting at what intensity various species begin singing. Of those studied, the field sparrow started at the lowest intensity—about .016 footcandles. The robin came next, then the catbird, song sparrow, cardinal, mourning dove, yellowthroat, house wren and finally the meadowlark at .08 footcandles. This was quite a range in the light intensity that triggered the various songs [14]. Another complication in singing is doing it with the mouth full. A bird will sometimes sing when carrying building material or food for the young. It is a little like a ventriloquist smoking a cigarette while he is "talking."

Amount of Singing / Many birds sing primarily in the early morning and perhaps in the evening; however, some species keep at it all day. We mentioned the red-eyed vireo that sang 22,197 times between dawn and dark. Other species that do not keep it up all day may sing very steadily while they are at it in terms of songs per hour. A grasshopper sparrow, for example, did 220 per hour and a Kirtland warbler 305 [4, p. 160].

Development of Song

Birdcalls and birdsongs on the whole involve both genetic and learned elements. The call notes, at least for most perching birds, seem to be mainly genetic. If we take young birds when they are hatched and rear them in isolation in soundproof rooms where they have no opportunity to hear experienced birds of their species, most calls of the given species eventually appear in the normal sequence and timing. Experiments have included blackbirds, white-throated sparrows, meadowlarks and some shrikes [12]. It is probable that calls evolved earlier than song. With this longer history, perhaps they have become more firmly fixed. Some authorities go so far as to say that calls are genetic and songs are learned, but this probably is too sharp a dichotomy. Most experts would find at least some genetic elements in the song.

With reference to song, most experiments bring out both innate and acquired aspects. The bird seems to inherit a tendency to certain patterns and then modifies them somewhat through experience. Some authorities say that the bird inherits the pattern and learns the quality, but it probably is not that simple.

Species seem to differ in the comparative genetic and acquired aspects of their song. Several species of buntings, for example, are reported to have songs that are highly stereotyped and "completely innate" [24]. Bluebirds, whitethroats and chaffinches reared in isolation developed a primary song motif that was not perfect but was somewhat similar to their regular song in duration and general quality—still, there was room for improvement. Again, individuals of a species do not develop identical songs unless they can hear each other. They seem to need this association in order to refine the original effort into the final repertoire [12]. The chaffinch alone gave a very poor, restricted version of the species song, but when reared with other young chaffinches it did better. When a group of young birds are raised together without hearing any outside song from experienced birds, they develop a fairly uniform pattern but not necessarily the typical wild song. On the other hand, if they are reared with another species and do not hear their own, they may imitate that species to some extent, although they still are somewhat partial to their own species, as was demonstrated with some white-crowned sparrows [12]. So while genetic elements are undoubtedly present in birdsong, there is plenty of evidence for some modification in the light of what the bird hears.

Young birds may get some tuition from their own parents during the first few weeks of life. Many parents still sing to some extent during the nesting period, which implies that the youngster can do some learning before it actually is singing itself. This was demonstrated with young meadowlarks which were exposed to certain recordings of meadowlark songs in June prior to their own singing. Those same patterns cropped out in their vocal efforts in September [12].

Theoretically this is somewhat surprising because it violates the principle of *learning by doing*. Pupils learn the multiplication table more readily if they repeat it aloud rather than just listen to it. Perhaps the birds do learn the song more readily when they try to sing it themselves, but evidently just hearing the parental song helps some. Then the young males perfect the finer details in their first breeding season the following spring, when they are actively competing with other males in advertising territory.

Critical Period / There appears to be a critical period in which learning of songs can take place. Experiments were made with white-crowned sparrows drawn from several populations that had appreciably different dialects, especially in the second part of the song. Birds were transplanted to other populations, that is, subjected to other dialects at various ages, or isolated at various ages to see what happened to their own ultimate songs. Spectrograms were used for the analysis. Young males captured between 30 and 100 days of age and kept in the aviary until the next spring sang their home dialect. Evidently in their first 30 days they were able to pick up this local dialect. If, however, they were captured between three and 14 days of age and thereafter isolated from their local dialect, the following spring they did not show that dialect although they manifested some species characteristics such as the sustained tone in the introduction of the song. Other experiments in which the birds were exposed to recorded songs of alien dialects had no effect if the recordings were presented when the birds were less than eight days old or more than 100 days [16]. Thus it appeared that there was a critical period within which hearing songs would influence how the bird sang subsequently.

It is possible that individual differences in learning ability play a role in this genetic-acquired aspect of birdsong. Some birds "catch on" more readily with various problems under laboratory conditions, so presumably some can learn songs more rapidly than others. The mimics, of course, such as mockingbirds, catbirds and some of the exotic birds like the parrot and the mynah bird, are especially adept in this respect. But the learning mechanism is ordinary conditioning, and saying "hello" implies no more intelligence or insight than pecking at a target.

Another factor that makes for some difference in the perfection of birdsong may be called "vocal inventiveness." Birds will try minor variations and experiment as it were. There are indications that there is more of this inventiveness in an acoustically "richer" environment. Oregon juncos were raised by hand in different degrees of acoustic isolation. All of them developed some wild-type songs, but most of the songs were longer than those in the wild species. However, birds in the richer environment, that is with more sounds available, had more song types and more elaborate syllable structure. This was not due to direct imitation, because sometimes the rich environment did not involve other junco singing at all. It seems that the varied environment stimulated their inventiveness [17].

We see, therefore, that in communication among birds the calls and songs and to some extent the postures do facilitate a good deal of the social behavior that has been discussed. We shall now turn to another aspect of social behavior, that involved in nesting and in the family situation.

CHAPTER IX

Home and Family Life of Birds

H*ere and there, in preceding chapters,* we have mentioned behavior connected with mating, nesting and raising a family. Now it is in point to pool these materials and present a more detailed discussion of some aspects.

TERRITORY

USUALLY the first consideration for the male bird in this family sequence is the territory in which he is to operate. With people, the usual practice is to get the girl first and then think about a home, but with birds it is the other way around. The male chooses the location for his establishment before he is even interested in females and when he has no notion who she is going to be. There are exceptions, however. Some birds mate permanently and even operate in the same region year after year. Others pick up a mate during the actual migration flight and arrive at the breeding grounds with all arrangements made prior to setting up the territory. But the practice overwhelmingly is for the male to make this initial territorial selection.

NATURE / The nature of the territory varies with the species. Some birds nest in open fields, some in trees, some on rocky ledges. Few birds build deep in the woods but prefer the edges, possibly because it is easier to get out into the fields for some of the foraging. A few species, such as the grouse, the ovenbird, the veery and a few warblers, nest on the forest floor. On the other hand, the Blackburnian warbler nests in the top of a hemlock.

The territory depends somewhat on the use that is to be made of it. Perhaps it is to be used for nesting exclusively while food is obtained elsewhere. Some birds nest in colonies and the individual site may be just a small spot with little clearance between nests. Other territorial arrangements may include an area where the male can strut or otherwise display.

Food / As implied above, the territory may include an area where food is obtainable. Song sparrows and wrens, for example, select such facilities. But if the food is scattered this may require too large a territory so the birds like the terns and herons feed at a distance. There also are situations where birds have individual nesting territories but a neutral territory for feeding. Robins sometimes do this, keeping others away from the immediate region around their own nest but getting together amicably when foraging in the same yard. There are cases where there is a small nesting territory and a large separate feeding territory. The bird may defend both the nesting and the feeding areas. Some herons have just a few feet adjacent to the nest under their jurisdiction but monopolize a whole lakeshore for feeding. A kingfisher may claim half a mile of the stream for this latter purpose.

Size / It is possible to map territories by careful observation. The owner chases intruders until they get beyond a certain point and then stops. He has his own landmarks or boundaries although occasionally a territory is ill defined. A few typical sizes may be mentioned. The robin usually occupies less than half an acre, the song sparrow from 0.5 to 1.5 acres. The prothonotary warbler needs more—from 3.5 to 6.3 acres. The meadowlark attempts to hold as much as 22 acres and has a substantial policing job. The size of the territory also depends somewhat on natural boundaries. Song sparrows on an island will use a territory one-tenth as large as that which they claim on the mainland. If the island is small, there is no point in claiming some of the surrounding water, since nothing of interest is taking place out there, anyway.

Interspecific / Cases have been found where birds of different species occupy territories that are pretty close together. A robin and a blue jay nested in the same pine tree, about 35 feet apart. Usually, these species are hostile and the jay sometimes destroys the robin's eggs, but on this particular occasion, there was an abundance of inchworm larvae nearby and also a well-stocked feeding station under the tree. Thus, the jay did not need robin's eggs or young for food, and the two species got along all right in close proximity [21].

Permanence / The usual procedure is to select a new territory and build a new nest every year. Frequently, the old nest gets broken up anyway. House sparrows do not migrate and frequently use the same nest site or may have two sites a few yards apart and use them indiscriminately. Some species keep the same territory year after year and reuse the same nest if it is suitable. Some species of albatross hold their territory for life and have a strong attraction to it—so strong, in fact, that if someone moves their eggs or chicks more than two yards distant they will desert the whole project [18].

Territorial Behavior

Advertising / Once a territory is selected, it must be established by advertising the fact and by defending it, that is, by singing and fighting. In the initial stage, the efforts are concerned primarily with the territory as such. With some species, such as grouse, the males are actually hostile to the females in the early stages and have been known to kill a female that entered the territory prematurely. Later, after the other males are under control, the incumbent becomes more gentle and interested in any female that comes along. However, there are exceptions. Male gadwalls are concerned with defense of the female rather than with defense of the territory from very early in the procedure.

Perch / The typical bird does its advertising from some conspicuous perch such as a treetop. The grasshopper sparrow uses the tallest weed in the field or a fence post. A red-wing once nested in the writer's shrubbery and perched in a high elm tree across the road. Whenever the writer came out to cut the grass, the red-wing buzzed him. Usually the song from the perch will take care of the territory without a fight. We have noted elsewhere, how posture may be a substitute for actual contact, and song operates likewise. The bird may sing louder as the intruder gets closer. A little later in the sequence the bird may move to a lower perch which is less conspicuous. Advertising is less necessary at that time when the territory is pretty well established. The purple martin uses a variation in territorial singing: it flies out from its house in a wide circle that ends in a steep dive with sudden braking and then it enters a compartment and sticks its head out and sings vigorously. All this is part of the general territorial announcement.

Fight / Often it does become necessary to fight for the territory or at least to dash after the intruder. Perhaps the dash may suffice, since it seems as if morale is better for the defender. Occasional mistakes are made in recognizing the intruder, such as attacking one's own reflection. A song sparrow, for example, sang from a hedge near the house, came down to the feeder and saw its own reflection in the window. Then it fought every downstairs window on that side of the house.

Most of the competition for territory is with other members of one's own species. Occasionally, it is otherwise. A song sparrow chased a kinglet and some other small birds but tolerated the larger ones. When an English sparrow and a goldfinch ignored the song sparrow's threat, that is, "called its bluff," it simply ignored them [15, p. 10].

As indicated above, the boundary line for the territory is rather well established by the holder of the territory. If invaders also learn where the line is drawn, there frequently may be some activity along that line. With the cactus wren, for example, both parties come up to the line and move slowly along it in parallel for 15 or 20 feet and then return. Bits of song or threatening posture are engaged in during this process, but there is actually no quarrel unless one crosses the line. Mockingbirds do something of the sort but give short hops backward and forward or sidewise in the vicinity of the line.

There is less aggressiveness in cases where nesting is somewhat semicolonial, as with the house finch, which is really aggressive only in the immediate vicinity of the nest and otherwise just mildly aggressive in song and in behavior.

The female goldfinch rather than the male selects the territory. Sometimes the female is more concerned with the territory, whether or not she selected it, than she is with the male. If a stronger male comes along and ousts her partner, that is all right with her as long as she keeps the territory. This situation also has been observed with robins, red-wings and house wrens. Another queer bit of behavior occurred when a pair of partridges actually put the nest outside the territory that had been established. Evidently, they did not take the initial territory very seriously. After this territorial business is settled, the birds are ready for the next step.

Courtship

Sometimes the procedure from this point on is relatively simple. The female happens into the established territory, is recognized as a female, is accepted at first sight and reciprocates. In some cases, however, there may be a problem in recognition if the sexes look alike. We mentioned previously the song-sparrow male that chases a newcomer and if the latter crouches down, knows that it is a female. Terns have the same problem but a different solution. Individuals take a small fish and pass it back and forth, often during flight. If the male gets back on his territory with the fish and offers it to another tern and the latter accepts, under those circumstances it is definitely a female and romance may begin.

Posture / Usually making up a congenial pair requires a little more doing than this mere recognition. Posture, or gesture, discussed in the preceding chapter on communication, is pertinent here and may communicate sex interest. Some of the gestures are terrestial and some are aerial. We shall discuss the former first.

Perhaps the male is still involved in aggressive posturing in connection with his territory. The female who happens along may counter by turning her head away, which is quite the opposite of fighting back, or she may crouch down. Sometimes she acts like a juvenile, quivering the wings and ostensibly begging for food. If this works, the male may feed her something, and then and there rapport is established. Feeding a female may take place quite apart from this initially hostile situation, such as when a pair of cardinals are feeding on the ground and he moves over and pops a bit of corn into her beak. The white-breasted nuthatch and evening grosbeak will thrust a sunflower seed toward the female. Of course, birds have no monopoly on this approach. We take her out to dinner or merely to a drugstore for a malted milk and/or a hamburger and this is quite routine. But with birds the performance is definitely ceremonial rather than nutritional. A female robin will beg from a male when she is standing in a tray of live mealworms.

If the male has some conspicuous feature in his plumage, he is apt to display that for the benefit of the other sex. The red epaulet of the red-wing blackbird is a case in point. The bowerbird holds the head sideways in order to show its crest. The peacock has an attractive tail and does the obvious thing. A species of bird of paradise actually hangs upside down so that gravity can facilitate the caudal display. The grouse spreads its attractively marked tail. Species with white in the wings spread them. Some birds like the male redstart, fluff their feathers to show the colors a little more effectively.

Quite a few gestures are made with the head. In gulls, a pair face each other and the male turns his head away. If the female does likewise, that is it. Another significant pose is with the bill lowered, which may have developed from picking up nesting material and thus could have some symbolic significance. In fact, they sometimes actually do pick up nest material, the male presenting bits of straw or grass to the female. We noted earlier how the penguin presents a small stone. Again, the male may carry a bit of nesting material around conspicuously, as is characteristic of mockingbirds and red-wings. The former actually places the material in various locations around the territory and keeps this up until the female stops and takes notice. However, she decides the actual nest site regardless of where he has been tentatively placing materials. In any case, he got her interest.

One of the most elaborate procedures along this line is carried out by the bowerbird. One species constructs a little stage carpeted with ferns and decorated with bits of bamboo, beetle skeletons and snail shells. On this stage, he struts around and displays. Others build an elaborate bower of sticks quite nicely decorated. When a female approaches, the male assumes an infantile posture, flattening the body, fluttering the wings like young begging for food and perhaps chewing on a bit of vine [9]. This is the reverse of the procedure described above, where the female does the begging, infantile routine.

Waterfowl such as ducks do a lot of their courting on the water, naturally. This may involve bobbing the head up and down quite rapidly or splashing about. The goldeneye kicks up a squirt of water behind him. The booby sticks the head, tail and both wings up as high as they will go.

One other procedure is common with a few species. The males gather in an appropriate place and display collectively. The ruffs —one of the shorebirds—gather in a field, each male with a territory about two feet in diameter. When a female comes along, they all stick out their conspicuous neck plumage, which is a sort of ear tuft, and pose. The female looks them over and makes her choice and so indicates by pecking at the neck feathers of the fortunate male [9].

The prairie-chicken males add something to the foregoing. They gather on a booming ground at dawn, inflate the air sacks at the sides of the neck and boom and jump up in the air and bump each other. The sharp-tailed grouse gives about the same performance without the bumping. With wild turkeys the males pay more attention to each other than to the females, strutting and displaying and gobbling a lot. The female that comes along has to more or less take the initiative in order to divert their attention from the intermale rivalry.

A species of albatross gives the female a little more participation in the ceremony. Four or five males form a circle with the female in the center. She faces each one of them in turn and the two perform a sort of dance. In this dance, the male is the more active and stretches to his full height with his wings half-spread and then finally fully open and then with his bill straight up. Each male in turn is given his chance to perform in this way with the female, and after they have all participated, she makes her choice. The rejects go off and join other circles and hopefully may get chosen eventually.

IN THE AIR / Some birds instead of doing their courting on the ground take to the air. The woodcock flies up to a height of 70 feet or so about dusk and after circling does a long dive. There is a characteristic whistling sound as the air goes through the feathers at the end of the wing and there are also some bubbling notes. On the ground between flights he gives a raucous sound. The horned lark goes up so high that it is difficult for a person to see him; he sings and plunges back to the ground. The snipe does something of the sort also. Hopefully some female may be impressed by these performances. The male marsh hawk does a loop-the-loop over the spot where the female is on the ground and sometimes does several loops in succession. Bobolinks fly to quite a height and then drop with the wings folded until they are near the ground, much like the parachutist who does not open the chute for some time after leaving the plane. These displays are obviously for the benefit of possibly watching females who later may make a choice. Grackles actually do some pair formation during flight. The female takes off and several males follow her. We do not know the rest of it because we do not accompany them on the trip, but when they return something has happened because a male and a female are flying close together and the others are some distance behind [8].

Song / The territorial song may have some interest for a female at the appropriate stage—at least it may attract her attention and bring her to the territory, where other procedures may supplement the song, which may now be directed at her specifically. Some of the rituals described above involve some singing. One study did show the impact of the male song on the female. An electronic device was installed in a house wren's nest box to record the pulse rate of the occupant. A female was on the nest and every time a male sang nearby her pulse rate increased. It is probable that this was an emotional response, because it occurred very consistently and research elsewhere has indicated that vascular changes operating through the sympathetic nervous system are sometimes correlated with emotional conditions [1, p. 159]. This response however, was not part of courtship because things were farther along, but it did indicate the emotional impact of the male's song. Similarly, with the red-winged blackbird, the female was observed to quiver her wings when the male sang—probably an emotional response.

We might mention a couple of instances where the female bird takes the initiative. The female spotted sandpiper often makes some of the initial approaches, and the male in return does a good share of the incubation. The female hairy woodpecker drums on a tree to attract the male's attention, especially during the season when they are concerned with excavating a nest hole. She apparently selects the territory, as evidenced by the location of the trees used for her drumming [13].

Presumably birds show individual differences just like people do in their effectiveness at courtship activity. There are even indications that experience helps. Young female domestic pigeons were placed in a pen with older males and paired more quickly than when they were placed in a pen with younger males. It looked as though the older males were more sophisticated or at least had developed some behaviors that proved more quickly successful. Conceivably, some of these behaviors could have been learned in the course of experience with females in previous years [14].

Characteristics of Pairs

Stability of Pair / Now that the birds are paired off, the question arises as to whether it is " 'til death us do part." We find a variety of answers. Sometimes it does look like the real thing and the pair seems quite devoted or at least attentive to each other. In the case of some evening grosbeaks, if the female was caught in a trap, the male stood beside the trap or on top of it and drove other males away. When the trap was taken inside the cabin by the operator for banding purposes, the male came in the window or door and stayed near until the operation was over, whereupon the pair flew away together. There were six cases where this pattern was followed. Again, eight birds of each sex on the ground were suddenly startled. They flew in eight directions—two birds in each direction [17].

There *are* permanent unions. It is generally agreed that this is the case with eagles and hawks, many of which do not face the hazard of getting separated during migration because they stay in one region the year around. There is some evidence of permanent union in the case of robins, swans, geese, common terns, some species of crow, nuthatches, creepers, some gulls and some ducks. Some chickadees have been observed to mate permanently [4]. Even the lowly house sparrow, contrary to popular notion, normally mates for life and generally uses the same nest or perhaps two nest sites close together. With Canada geese, if one member of the pair is killed, the other may remain single for years, whereas with most species, if one member is killed the survivor gets a new mate promptly.

Most species do not operate in pairs very much after the young have been raised, but some do keep together beyond the breeding season. The white-breasted nuthatch and the cardinal seem to do this, but whether they continue into the following years is not known. Many times the pair does not deliberately mate for life but find each other again during migration or return to the original area and blunder into the same former partnership. They may not even recognize each other too well until after they are paired.

In the less stable unions, the typical tendency is to stick together during the nesting season and then end the relationship permanently. There also are males who have a sort of fling, that is, take on several mates before a permanent union and family responsibilities. A male song sparrow, whom we shall call A had two mates. One was killed and then he stole his third one from another male called B. Then B, in turn, stole a mate from a third male, C, and presently C found an unattached female without any stealing.

Many bird species are polygamous. This is reprehensible by our standards but not by theirs, and in the wild it is common. We happen along occasionally at the right time to observe an instance and are duly impressed. For example, a starling at Cornell defended three nesting sites at once, had two females all season and had a third one for a few days. A wren in the writer's back yard raised two families at once in two nesting boxes. In more extreme cases the pair is together for only a few days, perhaps until the eggs are laid. Going still farther, the prairie chicken and sage grouse pairs separate almost immediately after mating, but these experiences are not traumatic to the birds to any observable extent. The important thing biologically is fertile eggs.

Hybrids / In mating, birds do not cross species lines very often. As noted elsewhere, they generally observe differences in plumage or behavior or song and thus are able to stick to their own species. In some species this is facilitated by imprinting (see Chapter VI). Occasionally they do cross however, and the hybrid may inherit antagonistic behaviors from the two parents, as well as queer plumage. These antagonistic behaviors may constitute a serious handicap to the bird, as in the case of a hybird of a redhead duck and a shoveler duck. In normal courtship, diving ducks like the redhead throw their head back toward the tail, while dabblers like the shoveler stand up in the water with their head down on the breast and grunt or whistle. A hybrid from this combination had both tendencies and tried to combine them when he reached the courtship stage. He rose in the water like the shoveler but threw his head back like the redhead. This did not make sense to the other ducks and nobody paid any attention to him, so he did not find a mate.

Similarly, a male hybrid of a prairie chicken and a sharp-tailed grouse boomed like a chicken and the other chickens approached. Then the hybrid raised his tail and danced like a grouse. The other chickens could not make this out and lost interest. He was not taken into the group that was to exhibit for the benefit of the females, so he too was doomed to celibacy.

Nesting

Site / After courtship, the next stage is nesting. Species differ in the location of the nest; it may be on the ground, in low bushes, high bushes, lower branches, high branches, treetops or holes. Sometimes the bird returns to the site of the previous year, even the same nest. Barn swallows do this quite consistently and thus save some time and are able to raise more broods in a given season. Some large birds of prey keep the same nest for years and add to it each season. The eagle does this and eventually gets a nest that may be 12 feet in diameter and weigh two tons. More generally, however, the bird has a new nest site, and of course there is always the first time for a young bird, many of whom return to the general area where they were hatched. About 40 per cent of the young gulls return to their natal area on the Great Lakes, and the percentage would be larger if the islands where they nest in colonies were large enough. Robins usually select a new site for their second nest in a given season, as did 23 out of 29 pairs of robins observed. We should be careful when watching a robin's nest that is used throughout the season, for it may not be occupied by the same incumbents for the second brood.

There is also the question of who selects the nesting site. The male has the territory staked out and the nest will, with a few exceptions, be within that territory. Usually the decision as to the actual location within the territory is made by the female. Some shorebirds, however, like the killdeer, do it the other way and the male makes the decision.

We do have some cases where the male tried to jump the gun but usually unsuccessfully. We mentioned elsewhere the male house wren that filled all the wren boxes in the neighborhood with sticks, which the female threw out when she arrived. The male long-billed marsh wren builds several nests before the female arrives, and she does not use any of them. At any rate he tried.

A number of considerations are important in the selection of the nest site. Some of these, such as food, are taken care of by the prior selection of territory. Another consideration is safety from predators, which has implications as to the height above the ground if the predator is terrestial. Woodpeckers have a special problem of finding a tree with sufficient internal decay so that it is easy to excavate. The redstart is particular about the kind of branch arrangement in the tree and requires a spot where three or more branches meet. The female does much exploring, starting at the base of a small sapling and working upward. She stands in a crotch and sometimes tests it by squatting down and rotating her body. She may in this way try 20 spots before making a final choice [7]. In a marsh some species have the problem of finding a location sufficiently up out of the water.

Some species build nests for roosting or sleeping as well as breeding. The cactus wren starts the year with two roosting nests and then the male and female collaborate in building the breeding nest. While the female is incubating the eggs, the male builds a second nest, which may be used for the second batch of eggs at the discretion of the female [2].

If the nest site is in a colony, the general area has already been determined and most of the decisions made, and it is then a matter of finding a small spot in the colony. House sparrows have colonies and defend just a very limited nest site, but this does involve a good deal of chattering in the ivy. A more complicated arrangement is that of the weaverbird in Africa, which builds something like apartments with up to a hundred pairs of birds in the one big construction resembling a haystack. A parakeet in Argentina makes a collective dwelling of sticks that accommodates up to 20 families.

MATERIAL AND CONSTRUCTION / Nest building is largely genetic, and the behavior follows the pattern for the given species.

This response can be touched off even at a tender age long before the bird is capable of breeding. A juvenile song sparrow, for instance, feeding in soft soil settled down into a dog track, pressed its breast against the side, kicked back with the feet and picked up a bit of dried grass and tucked it under the body [12]. On the other hand, there may be some modification of the instinctive pattern. We mentioned the weaverbird learning just when to let go of a piece of material it had pulled through the woven portion. Young ravens, building their first nests, are uncertain about material. They pick up the wrong size and type of stick but catch on very readily. The urge is there obviously.

There is a wide variety in the types of nests constructed. This is not of much concern to us in the present connection, but it might be mentioned in passing that when the nest is built in a hole, about two-thirds of the families succeed in raising a brood, whereas in open nests, only about half of them are successful. The material used in construction varies, including such things as straw, sticks, thistledown—and hair, although with the last there is the problem of finding an adequate supply. In one case a pair of opposums were sitting in an oak tree and a female titmouse was observed to land on one and pluck hair from the back, rump or base of the tail. She made something like 300 landings on one or the other animal. Altogether, she pecked at the pair about 1500 times and presumably gathered at least that many hairs. Evidently the opossums just "took it" and did not resist or leave. Titmice have also been known to collect hairs from the red squirrel and the woodchuck [10].

The techniques of building nests involve such things as weaving materials, rounding the cavity, lining it or excavating a hole in a tree. We just mentioned the young song sparrow going through the motions in a track in the mud. A young olive-backed thrush held by an experimenter in his cupped hands pushed its breast against the hand by kicking backward with the feet, then turned to a new spot and repeated the procedure. If the man applied a gentle pressure in one place, the bird would work harder at that spot but stop when he released the pressure. All this behavior evidently was built in.

A few queer nests might be mentioned. The whip-poor-will and the woodcock just scrape together a few leaves on the ground or maybe settle down where the leaf cover is thick enough to require no scraping. Some shorebirds lay their eggs on bare sand with possibly a few bits of straw nearby. Other birds have practically no nests at all. The fairy tern in the Pacific balances its egg on the branch of a tree, and the young birds have sharp claws with which they are able to hang on as soon as they are hatched. A nighthawk sometimes builds on a gravel roof and does not even bother to scoop a hole in the gravel. The egg may move as much as six feet but that does not disturb the parent. Some seabirds lay their eggs on the bare rocks on a cliff.

The emperor penguin deserves especial commendation. The single egg is held on the webbed feet of the male and he squats sufficiently so that it is in contact with his body, the air temperature being 40 to 70 degrees below zero. The male holds the egg in that fashion for two months and loses 25 pounds or one-third of his weight in the interim. Then the egg hatches and the well-fed female returns from wherever she has been and takes over care of the young while the male departs for a belated meal.

Sexes / Species differ with respect to the comparative participation of the sexes in the nest building. Some alternatives may be mentioned: (1) In many species, including woodpeckers, swallows and waxwings, the male and female collaborate in gathering material and fashioning the nest. (2) The sexes collaborate but there is some specialization, as with the rook male doing the stick part and the female the cup and lining. (3) The male mourning dove gets the material and the female does the construction. (4) Both catbird parents gather the material but the female does the actual building. (5) The female really does the work but the male stands around and pretends to help. With Lapland longspurs the male is there continuously and occasionally picks up a bit of nesting material similar to what the female is using but drops it [6]. (6) The female does it all alone, as in the case of the hummingbird and the red-eyed vireo. Sometimes the male makes a prior attempt at a nest, which is rejected. (7) The male is not even in evidence during the building. (8) The male does the building alone, as with some shrikes and some phalaropes. In the latter the sexes are reversed in the sense that the male builds the nest and incubates the eggs while the female is more conspicuous in plumage. (9) No nest is built at all, as in the case of the penguin just mentioned.

Incubation

About the time the nest is completed, the eggs arrive and somebody must incubate them, a procedure that begins usually after all the eggs are laid, which sometimes requires a few days. If incubation started on the first day and then some other eggs appeared a couple of days later, the first one would hatch earlier and that bird would be larger and would get most of the food.

The tendency to incubate is instinctive enough, but stimuli during the process may influence the program somewhat. The female bird usually has a brood patch on the breast where the feathers are thinner so the eggs can practically touch the bare skin and thus get more body warmth. Reciprocally, the temperature of the egg may stimulate the temperature organs in the parent's skin. An experiment was made with a herring gull by cooling the eggs to 77 degrees, whereupon the bird stuck very close to the eggs and was not easily frightened from the nest. When the temperature of the eggs was raised to 86 degrees, the bird was not so "faithful" [3]. Evidently, the instinctive tendency was to remain close when it was really necessary to transmit warmth to the egg. Beyond this, the bird sometimes gets visual and tactual stimuli from the nest, and possibly the hormones have some effect, too. In one case, these hormones evidently went wild and led a blue jay to sit on an empty robin's nest in December in Indiana. The bird went through typical incubation motions, rising slightly, probing the nest with the beak, shifting laterally as it settled down. It continued to do this the whole afternoon, though no external stimulus could be observed [16].

One parent must be on the nest most of the time. It may be possible to record the time automatically on a tape, as is easily done with a wood-duck nesting box arranged so that the bird touches a string when entering or leaving the hole. In one study, the periods on the nest averaged 19½ hours, with some of them as long as 60. The average periods away from the nest averaged 1½ hours, with the longest 5¼ [19]. With black-capped chickadees, the female was generally on the eggs from 18 to 27 minutes and off from seven to eight minutes. The male sometimes feeds the female while she is incubating, as in the case of blue jays and goldfinches. In one species of hornbill the male plasters up the entrance to the nesting cavity with mud and feeds the female through a hole; he also feeds the young through the hole when they arrive. Then at the proper time, he disinters the family by knocking out the plaster.

The birds stop incubating, of course, when the eggs hatch, but if the eggs fail to hatch in the normal period, the birds may keep at it, frequently up to twice the normal period. There was an extreme case of a male bobwhite that sat on 13 eggs from July 18 to October 7.

The total incubation time varies with the species. In general, it is longer for the larger eggs. Robins take 13 days, some ducks 21 to 30 and geese 30 to 35. The bird has no control over this, of course, and just keeps at it until it gets results.

WHO DOES THE INCUBATING / The most common practice is for both parents to share the incubating although they do not necessarily take turns in a strict alternation. If we consider all the bird families in the world, something like 54 per cent of them involve incubation by both parents, 25 per cent by females alone, 6 per cent by males alone, and 15 per cent by the female, the male or both. When both parents participate, there may be a little ceremony at the change of shift. The common egrets do a little dance at this time and then the one that is going off duty presents a twig to the incoming parent.

A possible advantage of the female doing all or most of the incubating is that she is more drab and less conspicuous on the nest to a predator. It may be noted that in the phalarope genus, the female is more brightly colored and the male does all the incubating.

COMMUNAL NESTS / There are a few reported instances of social nesting where more than one family share the same facilities. Two female wood ducks, for example, had a clutch of 13 eggs between them in a nesting box. Sometimes one, sometimes the other and sometimes both incubated the eggs. It is not known who laid the eggs originally but at least there was a collaboration afterward. This communal aspect is actually a species characteristic in the tickbird or ani in the tropics. They build a bulky affair of sticks in thorny bushes where several females lay eggs and take turns setting on them. They also collaborate later in feeding the young.

There are a few species that do not incubate the eggs at all. This perhaps reflects the reptilian ancestry of birds. An Australian species buries the eggs in a mound of earth and decaying vegetation that provides enough warmth. The parent birds return occasionally to uncover and turn the eggs. They also probe into the pile, evidently to check the temperature, and then add more vegetation or sand to control the temperature. If several families have eggs in the same pile, each female eventually takes charge of several chicks, although not necessarily her own [20].

A final consideration is to protect the nest from predators or other intruders. We noted elsewhere how the bird may try to decoy intruders away from the nest. If the predator is small enough, the bird may attack. Sometimes birds such as the woodcock rely on camouflage and pay little attention to the intruder while incubating, and one can almost pick up the bird, as has been described elsewhere. Again, some species run away from the danger but make an effort to conceal the eggs before they go, for example, by kicking sand over them. Then there are some species that if disturbed will abandon the nest altogether, which is one reason we are so worried about the condors in California. They are very sensitive to the intrusion of people and may abandon the nest if disturbed. There is a real danger that this species may become extinct, hence the efforts to keep people out of their nesting area. Other species that have this same tendency include herons, cormorants and mourning doves.

Care of Young

When the birds are hatched, the immediate problem then depends on whether they are altricial or precocial. If the former, they must be fed and protected from the sun or the cold. Brooding is part of the instinctive pattern for the parents or altricial chicks, but they do not show it very much unless the chicks are close to them. If the chicks are placed in an adjacent cage where they are inaccessible, the parents do not seem very disturbed about it. Normally, we expect a bird to brood just its own offspring, but this brooding tendency can be maintained for as long as six months by keeping the parents supplied with somebody else's chicks [5].

Precocial birds do not need any brooding and are practically ready to take off on their own responsibility, but sometimes there is a problem of getting them into circulation. Wood ducks are generally hatched in a nest in a box or a hole in a tree some 20 feet above the ground, and after from 20 to 36 hours they must be induced to jump out. They can not fly yet and have no parachutes. The female calls them from the ground and out they come. They are light and fluffy enough so that they land without damage, but actually they had been trained for this occasion. The mother gives a low *kuk, kuk, kuk* from the time the young are hatched until the time for the exodus. It is probable that they associate this call with her presence, which is rewarding in terms of comfort, so when they hear the *kuk, kuk, kuk* down below they go after it with the desired result [11].

Ground-nesting ducks may have something similar—at least the parents do considerable vocalizing in the first few hours. Perhaps the sound is an attention-getting device that presently leads the young birds to walk out of the nest.

There also is the matter of food—and plenty of it. We noted elsewhere how some young eat half their body weight daily. The techniques of feeding vary with the species and the stage of development of the young bird. Several situations may be mentioned: (1) The young are naked and blind and the parents put insects or worms in their mouths—many song birds; (2) the situation is similar except the birds have some down—the owls; (3) the eyes are open and the parents tear up the food rather than feeding them the whole rat—some hawks; (4) the youngster can walk but stays in the nest for a while and the parent brings food such as fish because the youngsters can not as yet catch fish themselves—gulls and terns; (5) the young birds follow the parents, who feed them—grebes and rails; (6) the young birds follow the parents, who show them the food and they peck at it themselves—quail; (7) the young birds follow the parents but find their own food—ducks and many shorebirds; (8) the young are completely independent of the parents—the megapodes of Australia.

Feeding the young is often shared by both parents. It is a pretty big job for one individual. The parents are not always as considerate as one might hope; the Laysan albatross, for example, does not feed the young unless they are fairly close to the nest even if it recognizes them. Mallard ducks were observed in a park where visitors threw food into the lake. The female adult gobbled up the food regardless of her young that were right alongside. We have already noted equivocal tendencies with colonial birds like penguins. Some parent birds feed the young indiscriminately and others feed just their own.

We should note that there is occasional cannibalism on the part of birds. In one case, there were seven young owls in a nest, three larger than the others. One pulled at the head of a smaller one, tried to swallow it and finally succeeded.

There is the final operation of protecting the young from predators. We have already mentioned fighting the predator or decoying it away. A minor precaution is the removal of bits of eggshell from the nest. If the shells are white, these remnants make the nest quite conspicuous from overhead.

All this business of raising young is a far cry from what is done at the human level but most of it seems to be reasonably successful. Under the circumstance, instinct is a pretty effective device after all.

CHAPTER X

Personality and Intelligence

Our discussion, thus far, has dealt

with the behavior of birds of a given species as if they were all alike. If we take our cue from psychology at the human level, this has been a major omission. Our intelligence tests are primarily devices for measuring individual differences. Personality measurements locate characteristics (extroversion, dominance, emotional stability) that make an individual unique and not just another faceless member of the species. These considerations have contributed to the solution of many practical problems. One school child, with low intelligence, is in the fifth grade, whereas another of the same chronological age but with a higher mental age is in the tenth. One criminal has delusions of persecution and another merely came from a home charged with undue emotional tension. One prospective taxi driver has slow reaction time and a high degree of emotional instability and is destined to have accidents, whereas another makes favorable scores on the aptitude test and is a good employment risk.

With birds, however, we have not looked into such implications of individual differences—in fact, we have not even looked at the differences as such. Theoretically we would expect birds of a species to range from high to low intelligence and from timid to aggressive because variability is characteristic of so many things in nature, but ornithologists have not been especially alert to these variables. There has been little experimental work on personality or intelligence, and field observations reported in books and technical journals give only an occasional pertinent opinion or anecdote. For example, if birds are being handled for some scientific purpose and one cowbird lies quietly in the hand and another bites, these differences in personality do not get into the record. It is probable that differences in personality and intelligence play more of a role than we suspect. At least, it may be worthwhile to take a look at such information as is available regarding these characteristics.

Let us begin with personality, which is to be distinguished from the bird's capabilities—not how fast it can fly but whether it actually does fly from the more aggressive member of its species. Oversimplifying the distinction somewhat, we could say that personality involves not a question of what the animal can do but rather what it will do.

Aggressiveness

Peck Order / One personality trait in birds that has been investigated to some extent is aggressiveness, a common manifestation of which, peck order, was mentioned briefly in Chapter VII. In a group of birds of a given species, one member tends to be dominant over the rest; another is second in rank and so on down the line. At the feeder Number One eats first and the others follow in turn.

Peck order can be observed and studied conveniently with birds in a laboratory or aviary or even a poultry yard. Considerable experimental work has been done with domestic fowl, presumably because they are more accessible, although some wild species, such as juncos, chickadees, Canada geese and pheasants, have been studied also in this respect. The peck order typically is a straight line A-B-C-D. A dominates all the others; B is subordinate to A but dominates C and D. Occasionally we find a triangular arrangement where A dominates B and B dominates C, but C dominates A [3]. We also find families arranged in a peck order with other families. This was the case with Canada geese [7] and with Oregon junco families [21].

Individual differences in aggressiveness doubtless underlie much of this, and the more aggressive bird is apt to land higher on the totem pole. There may even be a glandular basis because hormones influence emotional dispositions as was shown when starlings were injected with a certain pituitary hormone. When a subordinate starling was injected, he moved up in peck order rank [11]. In another experiment, hormone treatment of young chickens caused the peck order to develop earlier than it would have otherwise [6].

Other things besides aggressive personality influence a bird's rank. In poultry, the size of the comb and wattles, and even the bird's weight, affect his dominance. When comb and wattles were removed surgically, the bird assumed a lower rank [10], but we cannot be certain whether his appearance was now less impressive to his companions or whether his own awareness of his deficiency modified his aggressive behavior. Even such a factor as when a bird joined the flock may influence his position. When juncos were captured and put in an aviary together, those trapped earlier ranked higher in dominance than those trapped and added to the captive flock later. Of the earlier group, 14 out of 24 ultimately landed above the average in dominance, and of those added later 11 out of 18 (about the same percentage) were ultimately *below* average [21].

Usually the peck order is fairly stable, and there are seldom revolts against authority up the line. However, the tendency seems to vary somewhat with species. For example, Brahma hens do more revolting than some of the other domestic breeds. There are also situations where two birds happen to be very evenly matched, in which case those two particular ranks are very unstable and every now and then they have another fight and sometimes reverse rank. On occasion, the top-ranking bird takes his position rather seriously and makes obvious efforts to maintain it. With a species of sandpiper found in Australia, in a captive flock of more than 12 birds there were usually two that dominated. These two then herded the others into a corner where there were no perches or food tray and walked back and forth in a crouching position with feathers fluffed and legs bent, uttering a threatening *cheek*. Any bird that broke away from the corner was driven back and if he fell down was jumped on—two actually were killed. Evidently the top birds took steps to maintain their status and make it clear to all concerned who was in charge [22].

It is interesting to attempt experimentally to upset the peck order. One study involved a group of domestic fowl with the peck order well established. When eight of the birds were taken out individually and put in a cage with a foreign bird that was very despotic, each of them lost the fight. When they were returned to their own group, seven of the eight occupied a lower rank than they had before the outside fight. It is tempting to suggest that they felt more inferior after having been defeated by the outsider [20], but we do not know whether birds actually have inferiority feelings like we do. Perhaps the outside defeat merely reduced their inclination to fight in general. At any rate, there was an apparent change in aggressiveness.

In another experiment using a conditioning technique, wires were attached to the birds' wings so that they could be given a shock. The experimenter watched, and when the dominant member of a pair threatened or pecked at the subordinate member, the former was given a shock. After some treatment of this sort, the position of the two birds in the hierarchy was reversed. By an extension of this method to other pairs it was possible to change the A-B-C-D order to D-C-B-A [25]. Certain birds actually learned to assume a lower position, but whether the training influenced the bird's basic aggressiveness as such or merely changed it in the particular situation is problematical, although the latter alternative appears more plausible.

When we are observing birds with reference to the establishment of peck order, it is the fighting or threatening that we notice. Probably there are significant but less overt behaviors that do not catch our attention but that other birds can detect and act accordingly. It may be some subtle bit of posture similar to the way that we occasionally size up the personality of a person by the way he "struts."

Finally, it may be well to distinguish dominance in the peck-order sense from what might be called intolerance, which seems to be a spacing device to prevent undue crowding and may have some advantage in normal foraging in the wild by assuring that all the birds do not alight on the same bit of food simultaneously. It may be achieved or maintained in about the same way as dominance by pecking or threatening, but it is not aimed at subordinating the other party but merely keeping him at "arm's length," as it were.

Aggressiveness Without Fighting / Situations that call for aggressiveness are often handled without actual physical contact. Threatening posture may suffice, as was mentioned in Chapter VIII. A head-forward threat is almost universal among perching birds and is often accompanied by fluffing of the feathers and perhaps a slight spreading of the wings so that the bird looks larger. Some species use the head differently: an aggressive gull points the head straight up and a timid one points it down [26].

Another type of threat is to display whatever conspicuous plumage the bird has. A robin turns the red breast toward an opponent, the red-wing may show his epaulet, and the black-headed gull shows off his brown face. Coots lower their heads to show the white frontal plates, but also do some charging toward the enemy. Mockingbirds flash their white wing bars to make them more conspicuous, the white-breasted nuthatch does likewise right in the intruder's face and pectoral sandpipers move their head sidewise, which almost suggests that they are sparring. Gulls sometirnes resort to pulling up a lot of grass. Perhaps the bird is angry at the opponent but also afraid to attack, so he pulls the grass as an outlet. Hopefully the opposition gets the idea. An oceanic bird, the fulmar, actually spits on the enemy a sort of oily substance [18].

There also are songs and call notes that express hostility, much as we tell someone what we propose to do to him. The territorial singing discussed elsewhere is a good example. The behavior also extends to defense of the nest and young, but here again individual birds proceed somewhat differently [9]. With mockingbirds, for example, one male was zealous about singing day and night but let the female do most of the food gathering for the young. He was not pugnacious in nest defense. Another male, however, sang very little after the young were hatched but hunted food vigorously and guarded the nest pugnaciously. Both birds showed commendable aggressiveness but expressed it differently. Thus birds have a considerable variey of aggressive substitutes for actual fighting.

Individual differences / The differences in aggressiveness were studied with the British robin [8]. A stuffed model was used to touch off the behavior rather than a live opponent. Such a stimulus is constant, whereas a live one might differ in provocation, and also, the model stays put, whereas a real opponent might leave and the experiment would end. The situation produced a variety of behaviors. Some robins completely ignored the stuffed model, while others merely postured at it in a threatening fashion. Some postured and then actually attacked, and some attacked at the very outset without more ado. Thus there were obvious individual differences in aggressiveness, as there were variations in the type of posturing. Some birds gave a rather slow swaying of the breast and held the feet still while others jerked their head and breast and had a rapid foot movement.

Siblings / Fighting is not always confined to adults. The young of several species of eagles while still in the nest get pretty rough with each other. On occasion, an older nestling will kill a younger one. There is no obvious utility to this but at least it does indicate that aggressiveness develops rather early [14 p. 166].

Morale / Tinbergen says that a bird's success in fighting depends "almost entirely on morale." We are familiar with its importance in a military situation, so why not with birds? Actually, a bird seems to have the highest morale when it is defending its own territory. Almost always in a contest between a defender of territory and an intruder, the defender wins. The vigorous defense may be part of the instinctive pattern, but the one-sidedness of the usual contest suggests the presence of some other factor, which could be something analogous to morale.

Attacking Other Species / Aggressiveness may be directed toward other than one's own species. We have noted elsewhere how crows collectively threaten a hawk or an owl, and the crows, in turn, are tormented by kingbirds or even by red-winged blackbirds. These smaller birds maneuver so as to dive at the crow and even nip him occasionally. Birds presented with stuffed models of other species may attack them as if they were real and frequently demolish the model. Usually the birds do not destroy the model unless it has a head, which seems to be the vulnerable part.

Maneuverability / A factor that may influence the aggressiveness in a particular situation is the comparative ability of the two species to maneuver. A hummingbird, for example, has been known to attack a hawk. With its very rapid wing beat, the hummingbird can change direction rapidly and get around the larger bird without being vulnerable to attack itself [27]. The writer once observed an instance of this comparative maneuverability in the case of a red-shouldered hawk and a crow, crows usually being the aggressors. In ordinary flight, there is not too much difference in maneuverability and the crow makes a lot of passes at the hawk. In the present instance, however, there was a very high wind, and hawks do a great deal of gliding and are adept at taking advantage of wind currents even in a high wind. The crow, on the other hand, just lumbers along flapping his wings without much gliding and is unable to take advantage of currents. So our hawk simply turned the tables on the crow and became the aggressor, and for quite a few minutes, it circled around and made passes at the crow while the latter was trying to escape as best it could. The hawk's mate meanwhile was circling around above them and screaming encouragement, presumably. It was interesting to see the situation reversed simply by this temporary difference in maneuverability.

Attacking Other Animals / On occasion, birds will attack various animals other than birds, cats being one of the common victims. Even a hummingbird was observed to fly at a cat and stab at its face. The bird could stab and get out of range before the slower-moving paws of the cat could do anything in the way of defense, and the hummingbird actually injured the cat's eye. Many other species will threaten the cats around the neighborhood.

Attacking Humans / Birds even go so far as to attack people. A mockingbird attacked a particular woman repeatedly [9], following her a hundred yards and striking her on the back. She had been near the nest a bit previously, and the bird was able to single her out from a small group of other people and attack her rather than someone else.

A hawk will threaten a person who is at the nest for photographic or banding purposes. The parent bird screams and dives but does not actually hit the intruder. Eagles do likewise, but there have been cases where an eagle actually hit the person at the nest. In one case the man was not close to the nest at all but was down at the base of the tree looking at the nest above through a telephoto camera lens. He felt something brush against the side of his forehead and subsequently found a superficial scratch where the eagle made a pass at him but did not actually dig in [12].

In Scotland five birds of a species resembling the pheasant attacked people, automobiles, sheep and horses, but for some reason would not attack dogs. Each of these birds lived in a small woods near the road with no rivals of its own species, and it is possible that with the spring, they turned the aggressiveness that normally goes with territorial defense toward any large moving object. Two of them did it on four successive springs and one during five springs [4]. We should be careful, however, on this matter of birds attacking automobiles, because sometimes they see their own reflection in the hub cap and attack that, their apparent objective being another bird. It is possible also that these particular birds were unusually aggressive individuals.

Many scientists have been bitten by birds, and some of them may have noticed individual differences between their clients in this respect. One cardinal bites the hand that holds it and another does not, but we cannot be sure that the bird is attacking the person as such. Perhaps, as in any frustrating situation, it bites anything available. If one reaches into a gathering cage and extricates a handful of cowbirds for banding purposes, each one has a strong grip with its beak on some part of another's anatomy.

Attacking Eggs / Some birds manifest their aggressive behavior toward eggs. Sometimes, to be sure, the eggs are a staple food, but other times birds wreck the eggs for no ulterior purpose that can be determined. Grackles do this frequently, and house wrens are the most notorious hole punchers. However, even here we notice marked individual differences, for in some localities, all the wrens do it and in other localities, none do. Observations in one yard indicated that one wren ruined scarlet tanagers' and chipping sparrows' eggs while another wren lived peaceably with redstarts, robins and phoebes. [1, p. 130]

Redirected Aggression / Sometimes a bird gets so disturbed at one thing that it attacks something else it normally would not attack at all. In England when a stuffed yellow cuckoo was placed near a willow warbler's nest, the male attacked the model for about eight minutes, then the female attacked. Presently the male attacked the female and then went off and attacked his own reflection in some flashlight equipment. It would seem that he was just overwhelmed with rage at the stuffed cuckoo and the aggression was redirected toward other things, including his own mate [24].

SEASONAL / Aggressive behavior may be somewhat seasonal, being especially pronounced in the spring in connection with territory and nesting, as we have suggested elsewhere. It may be part of the whole sex-parental pattern, but it may carry over to other stimuli that are not actually a threat to the territory. A robin is very aggressive even toward a stuffed model at about the time when the young are beginning to get feathers [8].

SELF-SUFFICIENCY

WE may now turn to some other personality characteristics that have been less thoroughly studied, one of which might be termed self-sufficiency, involving such things as getting away in a hurry when there is danger or foraging in a wide variety of situations when food is scarce. The writer gets the impression that starlings are quite self-sufficient in this sense. One observation is pertinent in this connection. A large decoy-type trap was in operation near a "blackbird" roost. When a hundred or more were in the trap, they were chased down a long runway or funnel at one side of the trap into a gathering cage at the far end. The point of interest in the present connection is the comparative tendency of different species to lead the way into the funnel and away from the person chasing them. If there are several hundred birds in the trap, we cannot get them all into the gathering cage on one run. So we gather a goodly number on the first run, band them, and then chase some more. If the trap is filled primarily with starlings and cowbirds, the significant point is that on the first drive we get mostly starlings, then on the second and subsequent drives, the cowbirds pick up. In other words, the starlings are the ones that get away from the presumed danger in self-sufficient fashion. This survival behavior was observed again and again, and it may be part of the genetic pattern. The original starlings in Europe were persecuted by people for thousands of years and may have evolved a tendency of the sort that their descendants now manifest. At any rate, the behavior seems to reflect species differences in self-sufficiency, and there probably are individual differences, too, in this respect if we had techniques for discovering them.

Emotional Stability

There are some indications of differences in emotional stability among birds. We mentioned earlier a case of extreme rage wherein the bird attacked almost anything in sight, but it is doubtful that his behavior was typical of the species. There is also the case of a caged song sparrow that was placed, cage and all, in the territory of a rival; it went simply "wild" with fear. The bird on territory kept threatening and flying toward the cage, and presently, the outsider took hold of a tip of a wing through the bars and the caged bird died—presumably of a heart attack, although there was no autopsy. At any rate, it is highly probable that the extreme fear in that individual bird was enough to kill it [19, p. 138]. A field sparrow died shortly after being caught in a net and banded, possibly from emotional shock. If we had enough observations we might well find differences in emotional stability in birds comparable to that in humans.

It has been observed that emotional response varies also with the surroundings. Young goshawks in the nest will strike at a man who approaches the nest to band them or take pictures, attacking him with wings and claws. However, if they are put in a basket and lowered to the ground for photographic purposes, they become very quiet in the unfamiliar surroundings.

Tameness

Elsewhere we discussed tameness—becoming habituated to something that originally was frightening to the bird—as an aspect of learning. In the present context there are doubtless individual differences in tameness resulting from differences in experience rather than from some more basic factor, but with experience constant we may at times observe such differences. Some wild geese habituated to a game refuge are more wary than others and take flight earlier when someone approaches.

Similarly with robins nesting in the same vicinity, an occasional individual will remain on the nest incubating the eggs or brooding the young while a person walks up and touches the bird. Most of the parent robins leave when an intruder is several feet distant, although all of them, of course, tend to remain to a greater extent as part of the breeding-nesting pattern, but, even so, pronounced individual differences in tameness are apparent.

There are also species differences in tameness. Kinglets, titmice and chickadees are relatively tame and will come rather close to humans in the woods and even exhibit something akin to curiosity. One species of penguin will charge a man who approaches; another species moves away slowly; a third species stands still [13].

Some of these individual traits such as tameness or wildness may be rather permanent. In one example, the writer was holding a robin and examining a band on its leg. The bird was extremely excited and fought back vigorously. When the band number was looked up in the log, it developed that four years earlier when the bird was originally banded, there was a note to the effect that he was "extremely excitable." This personality characteristic had been sufficiently pronounced to warrant a note in the original record and four years later the robin showed the same tendency.

A study of some Carolina wrens indicated some individual consistency in personality. Ten of these birds were caught on two occasions in a mist net and then handled while being banded or having band numbers checked. Four of them squealed on both occasions, four squealed on neither occasion and two squealed on the first experience but not the second. Thus, eight of them were consistent [16].

The writer has occasion to handle numerous birds in the process of banding them at a decoy trap. Some of them return to the trap and get handled a second time. A study is in progress wherein each bird is rated on a ten-point scale for aggressiveness every time he is handled. The second rating of a bird is made without consulting his first rating. With grackles more than half the birds have the second rating very close to the first. More data are needed, of course, but there is a definite suggestion that the grackles are consistent in their degree of aggressiveness. This points toward fundamental individual differences in personality.

Abnormal Characteristics

Prolonged Immaturity / At the human level, something frequently goes wrong with personality and the bulk of our abnormal behavior falls under this category, but we have only limited information about birds in this respect. One characteristic that might be considered deviate is prolonged immaturity. We mentioned elsewhere how young robins just out of the nest differ considerably in seeking food, some chasing after their parents and begging vociferously, while their brothers and sisters forage for themselves. Similarly, three young cardinals perched near a feeder and screamed at their parents, who were eating. The parents then fed them, although they were capable of picking up the grain themselves. This routine continued for about six months.

An experiment was made to see just how far this delay in maturity could be pushed. Four young shrikes were raised by hand until they were old enough to pick up food and quit begging. Beginning at age 21 days, two of the birds had a supply of food kept in front of them and the hand feeding was gradually discontinued and stopped as soon as possible. At 28 days, they fed themselves all right although they still begged when the experimenter approached. At 39 days, they rarely begged and at 45, they were strictly on their own. The other two birds, beginning at 21 days, had no free food available but were fed completely by hand, the food actually being put into their mouths. They were tested periodically to see if they would feed themselves. At 28 days, there was no evidence of this at all. At 53 days, they made some effort to feed themselves by pecking food from the fingers and evidently could have been changed over at that time. However, the hand feeding was continued, and at 7½ months, they still begged although they would pick up any grain that was accidentally dropped, thus showing that excessive care can delay the loss of infantile behavior. With us, this delay in maturity is usually the parent's fault, as in the case of a mother who combs her son's hair until he finishes high school. Bird parents have not read the book about how to raise children and presumably treat all the nestlings about alike. Therefore the differences mentioned at the outset of this section presumably reflect some kind of innate personality difference.

SEX DEVIATIONS / Birds manifest some behaviors that at the human level would be considered sex deviations. The polygamous house wren was mentioned with his two simultaneous establishments in the same backyard, and one case has been recorded of "incest" on the part of a junco. A male junco was banded and had four nestlings that were banded likewise. The next year, the same male mated with one of the preceding year's nestlings and had two grandchildren [17]. Such behaviors are scarcely regarded as deviate with birds, since there is no avian morality or immorality.

PARASITISM / We have discussed parasitism as a type of anti-social behavior, but it should receive passing mention in the present context because in a sense it is "abnormal" too. The cowbird and some species of cuckoo lay their eggs in the nests of other birds who assume the responsibilities from that point on (see Chapter VII).

PSYCHOTIC BEHAVIOR / There has been little indication of actual psychotic behavior on the part of birds, the nearest thing to it perhaps being some observations of displaced emotional behavior when the bird is badly frustrated and tears things up in some fashion. A song sparrow in a cage had a rival alight outside whereupon the former bird pulled at strings and bit at straws in the cage seemingly taking his frustration out on anything available [15]. Grackles, jays and robins have been observed, when their nests were threatened, to attack branches of trees and grass when it was not feasible to do something about the actual source of the threat [23]. This may not be truly psychotic behavior but an abnormal response to the situation when the normal response is not feasible. Birds are not subject to the difficulties that so often produce maladjustment in humans, such as rivalry with brothers and sisters or the impact of a favorite child on the others. If such problems existed, the result might merely be a bit of aggressiveness but certainly not kleptomania. There is some doubt whether bird parents really "spoil" the youngsters or are unduly "brutal" toward them and thus set up lasting maladjustments that crop out in later life. Civilization may have its disadvantages.

GENETIC VERSUS ACQUIRED / There is a final question as to whether personality is innate or acquired, and probably both aspects are involved. In other animals such as rats, it has been possible to breed for aggressiveness merely by mating aggressive with aggressive and submissive with submissive. After several generations, the result is an extremely aggressive group and vice versa. This experiment has not been tried with birds but probably it would work. We mentioned a moment ago the robin whose excitable tendencies persisted for four years. On the other hand, we noted that the peck order could be modified somewhat by experience, for example, by giving the dominant bird a shock when it attacked a subordinate. There also was the deliberate prolongation of immaturity for the young shrikes. Thus we have some evidence that the birds probably are like us in that some aspects of personality are inherited and others picked up from experience.

INTELLIGENCE

WE now come to intelligence, the other major characteristic in which individual birds and species differ. Psychologists are much concerned with this at the human level, since it is involved in numerous practical problems. Intelligence does not play as large a role in birds and instinctive processes loom larger than they do with us. The fact that the bird can fly may have made some difference in this. Flight was a very successful evolutionary venture but it may have cost the birds a lot in the way of intelligence since many times they could fly away from a problem and if it had been necessary for them to stay and figure out a solution "or else," the brighter ones who did figure it out would have survived and, thus, a higher order of intelligence might have evolved. To be sure, mammals like ourselves run away from some problems but in general cannot go as fast or as far as the birds. If winged vertebrates can fly away from the problem instead of facing it and still survive, evolution has less of a chance. Perhaps we should be grateful that our ancestors did not have wings.

There are no available "intelligence tests" for birds, the nearest thing to it, perhaps, being the adaptability or rate of learning exhibited in some experimental situations. Some small sparrowlike birds in England had to go through a sequence of acts in the laboratory in order to obtain food. The experimenters stated that the birds showed individuality, some solving the problem at once and others seeming permanently defeated [2]. The authors of the report actually titled their article "intelligence tests," which is the only mention the writer has found in ornithological literature.

We might refer at this point to the earlier discussion of insight learning in Chapter VI. The use of "tools" in the form of sticks to dislodge insects from crevices looked at first like rather intelligent behavior, but we concluded that inasmuch as many of those finches used this method, it did not involve a "discovery" and conceivably could have evolved as a species characteristic. It may be noted further that birds of this species habitually hide seeds and the like in holes and crevices, and some of the movements used in extracting them with the bill resemble the movements made with the tool, and it is possible that the behavior with a stick is just an extension of the bill procedure. One of these birds was breaking off bark to get at grubs underneath and broke off a twig and carried it along while searching various branches but did not use it. Another species of finch used the stem of a leaf to probe in the crevices, but the leaf stem bent and after four attempts the bird dropped the stem. This was not a very astute performance, and the reports on these Galapagos finches do not indicate unequivocally a high level of intelligence.

Milk Bottle / Another performance that the uncritical observer might consider quite intelligent is a tendency for several species of birds in England to open milk bottles, or at least to contrive somehow to get at the milk. They use various techniques —tearing off the paper layer by layer, removing the top, punching holes in the cap. Some of the species that do this are accustomed to tearing bark off trees anyway and tearing paper is not so different. They could learn it by actually tearing at the cap when foraging for food and being rewarded by a drink of milk, or one bird might see another at the milk and come down and peck away much as he would do with a group at a feeder pecking at corn. We do not need to assume too much insight or intelligence in all this [5].

Species Differences / The psychologist studying intelligence at the human level is interested primarily in individual differences, but we are all of one species. With birds however, there is the additional possibility of noting differences between the various species. Evidence, however, is meager, although a food shortage may show up some differences in adaptability. A species of brant became nearly extinct along the Atlantic Coast when a blight took out the eel grass. Kites in the Everglades will not eat anything but snails and are hard put if there is a snail shortage. On the other hand, crows rise to the emergency, raid mouse nests for the young, eat animals killed on the highway and even fish. The case will be recalled of the crow that learned to reel in the fishline that extended through a hole in the ice. Some other birds have been taught a similar performance, but the crow did it without tuition—certainly a resourceful behavior.

Catbirds and mockingbirds are sufficiently adaptable to pick insects off car radiators, although this might possibly be merely an extension of ordinary foraging. A sparrow hawk, which ordinarily eats rodents, ate some bread crusts in lieu of rats.

Some ornithologists who have observed many species mention differences in intelligence. Welty remarks that parrots and crows are "birds of superior intelligence," in comparison with the "less intelligent fowls and pigeons" [28, p. 70]. Allen says that the black ducks and the goldeneyes are the most intelligent and wood ducks are the most stupid [1, p. 131]. His judgment is based primarily on the fact that when the birds are kept in a refuge with their wings clipped, most ducks have learned that they cannot fly and if alarmed run into the water, but wood ducks always try to fly anyway and often turn somersaults in the process. They apparently are less adaptable. Allen also gives crows credit for being "very intelligent."

If we consider young birds soon after they are hatched, we might erroneously assume some species differences in intelligence. Young ducks leave the nest shortly after they are hatched and strike out on their own, while many songbirds remain in the nest and are fed by their parents for some time. These differences in behavior depend on rate of development at the time of hatching rather than being attributable to inferior or superior intelligence. The songbirds catch up eventually, and their initial status does not reflect any basic species differences in intelligence.

One final thought. Implied in the foregoing discussion is the fact that birds can be interesting to a lot of people. Almost everyone likes to hear them sing and many of us enjoy watching their activities. This makes a good hobby, but you cannot pursue it unless you have some birds to watch. You will not find them around high-rise apartments, and only a few species can get along in thickly settled urban areas. It is much the same story for those of us who like to pursue wild flowers or trees or ferns. What we need are substantial areas where nature can run wild and we can go out to look or study. The tragic story of urban sprawl, megalopolis, bulldozers and the population explosion that is partly to blame has been spelled out elsewhere. So if we want our great-grandchildren to hear birdsongs on a spring morning, we had better give some serious attention to the preservation of our natural resources.

REFERENCE NOTES

CHAPTER II

1. Allez, R., and Boyd, H., "Parent-Young Recognition in the Coot," *Ibis,* 92:46–51, 1950.
2. Anon., *Science News Letter,* June 30, 1962, p. 409.
3. Baerends, G. P., "The Ethological Analysis of Incubation Behavior," *Ibis,* 101:357–68, 1959.
4. Blum, D., "Verhaltungsstudien an Grünspechten," *Vogelwelt,* 78:41–48, 1957.
5. Davis, S. J., and Carrick, R., "On the Ability of Crested Terns to Recognize Their Young," *Australian J. of Zool.* 10:171–77, 1962.
6. Erhard, H., "Messende Untersuchungen über den Farbensinn der Vogel," *Zool. Jb. Abt. Allg. Zool. Physiol.,* 41:489–92, 1924.
7. Farb, P., *American Forestry.* Cf. *Reader's Digest,* Sept., 1962.
8. Ficken, M. S., "Maintenance Activities of the American Redstart," *Wilson Bull.,* 74:153–65, 1962.
9. Frankel, A. T., and Baskett, T. S., "Color Marking Disrupts Pair Bonds of Captive Mourning Doves," *J. Wildlife Mgmt.,* 27:124–27, 1963.
10. Griffin, D. R., "Bird Sonar," *Sci. Amer.,* 190:79–85, 1954.
11. Guhl, A. M., and Ortmann, L. L., "Visual Patterns in the Recognition of Individuals Among Chickens," *Condor,* 55:287–98, 1953.
12. Hailman, P., "Pecking of Laughing Gull Chicks at Models of the Parent Head," *Auk,* 79:89–98, 1962.
13. Holst, E., and St. Paul, U. V., "Electrically Controlled Behavior," *Sci. Amer.,* 206:50–59, 1962.
14. Kaufman, I. C., and Hinde, R. A., "Factors Influencing Distress Calling," *Animal Behavior,* 9:197–204, 1961.
15. Kellogg, P. P., and Hutchinson, C. M., "The Solar Eclipse and Bird Song," *The Living Bird,* 3:185–92, 1964.
16. Laskey, A. R., "Breeding Biology of Mockingbirds," *Auk,* 79:596–606, 1962.

17. Lehtonen, L., *Biological Abstracts*, No. 36530, 1960. (Article in Finnish Journal.)
18. Miller, L., "Auditory Recognition of Predators," *Condor*, 54:89–92, 1952.
19. Mohr, H., "Erkennen von Raubvögeln insbesondere von Sperber und Baumvolk durch Kleinvogel," *Ztsch. f. Tierpsychologie*, 17:686–99, 1960.
20. Novick, A., "Acoustic Orientation in the Cave Swiftlet," *Biol. Bull.*, 117:297–303, 1959.
21. Owre, O. T., and Page, O. N., "Indications of Sense of Smell in Turkey Vultures from Feeding Tests," *Amer. Midland Naturalist*, 66:200–5, 1961.
22. Payne, R. S., "The Acoustical Location of Prey in the Barn Owl," *Amer. Zoologist*, 1:379, 1961.
23. Peterson, R. T., *The Bird* (New York: Time, Inc., 1963).
24. Rand, A. L., *Stray Feathers from a Bird Man's Desk* (New York: Doubleday, 1955).
25. Rand, A. L., Note in *Auk*, 68:524, 1951.
26. Rensch, B., "Experimentelle Untersuchungen über den Geschmacksinn der Vogel," *J. fur. Ornithologie*, 73:1–8, 1925.
27. Reynolds, G. S., and Catania, A. C., "Temporal Discrimination in Pigeons, *Science*, 135:314–15, 1962.
28. Rice, D. W., and Kenyon, K. W., "Breeding Cycles and Behavior of Laysan and Blackfooted Albatrosses," *Auk*, 79:517–67, 1962.
29. Schleidt, W., *et al.*, "Störung des Mutter-Kind Beziehung durch Verhörverlust," *Behavior*, 16:254–60, 1960.
30. Stager, K. E., *The Role of Olfaction in Food Location by the Turkey Vulture* (Los Angeles County Museum Contrib. to Science, No. 81, 1964, 63 pp.).
31. Tinbergen, N., *Bird Life* (London: Oxford University Press, 1954).
32. VanTyne, J., and Berger, A. J., *Fundamentals of Ornithology* (New York: John Wiley, 1959).
33. Walls, G. L., "The Vertebrate Eye and Its Adaptive Radiation," *Cranbrook Inst. Sci. Bull.*, No. 19, p. 295, 1942.
34. Waters, R. H., *et al.*, *Principles of Comparative Psychology* (New York: McGraw-Hill, 1960).
35. Welty, J. C., *The Life of Birds* (Philadelphia: Saunders, 1962).
36. Zimmerman, J., and Feister, C. B., "Chained VI Performance of Pigeons Maintained with an Added Stimulus," *J. of the Exper. Analysis of Behavior*, 7:83–89, 1964.

CHAPTER III

1. Allen, A. A., *The Book of Bird Life* (Princeton: Van Nostrand, 1961).
2. Annan, O., "Experiments on Photoperiodic Regulation of the Testis Cycle in Two Species of the Thrush Genus *Hylocichla*," *Auk*, 80: 166–74, 1963.
3. Bayer, E., "Beitrage zur Zweikomponententheorie des Hungers," *Ztsch. f. Psychologie*, 112:1–54, 1929.
4. Darling, F. F., "Social Behavior and Survival in Birds," *Auk*, 69:183–91, 1952.
5. Dorst, J., *The Migrations of Birds* (Boston: Houghton Mifflin, 1961).
6. Engels, W. L., "Migratory Restlessness in Caged Bobolinks," *Biol. Bull.*, 123:542–54, 1962.
7. Farner, D. S., "The Photoperiodic Control of Reproductive Cycles in Birds. *Amer. Scientist*, 52:137–55, 1964.
8. Frings, H. and M., "Bio-Acoustics and Pest Control," *Bio-Acoustics Bull.*, 2:21–24, 1962.
9. Grindley, G. C., "Experiments on the Influence of Reward on Learning in Young Chickens," *British J. Psychology*, 20:173–80, 1929.
10. Hamilton, J. B., "Precocious Masculine Behavior Following Administration of Synthetic Male Hormone Substance," *Endocrinology*, 23:53–57, 1938.
11. Holst, E., and St. Paul, U. V., "Electrically Controlled Behavior," *Sci. Amer.*, 206:50–59, 1962.
12. Lofts, B., and Marshall, A. J., "Zugunruhe Activity in Castrated Bramblings," *Ibis*, 103:189–94, 1961.
13. Rand, A. L., *Stray Feathers from a Bird Man's Desk* (Garden City: Doubleday, 1955).
14. Tolman, C. W., "Social Facilitation of Feeding Behavior," *Animal Behavior*, 12:245–251, 1964.
15. Weise, C. M., "Migratory and Gonadal Responses of Birds on Long-Continued Short Day-Lengths," *Auk*, 79:161–72, 1962.
16. Wolfe, J. B., and Kaplan, M. D., "Effect of Amount of Reward and Consummative Activity in Learning in Chickens," *J. Comparative Psychology*, 31:353–61, 1941.

CHAPTER IV

1. Allen, A. A., *The Book of Bird Life* (Princeton: Van Nostrand, 1961).
2. Allen, A. A., *Stalking Birds with Color Camera* (Washington: National Geographic Society, 1951).
3. Berger, A. J., *Bird Study* (New York: John Wiley, 1961).
4. Colias, E. C. and N. E., "The Development of Nest Building Behavior in a Weaver Bird," *Auk*, 81:42–52, 1964.
5. Cruze, W. W., "Maturation and Learning in Chicks," *J. Comparative Psychology*, 19:371–409, 1935.
6. Davies, S. J. F., "The Orientation of Pecking in Very Young Magpie Geese," *Ibis*, 103a:277–83, 1961.
7. Dow, D. G., "Diving Times of Wintering Water Birds," *Auk*, 81:556–57, 1964.
8. Ficken, M. S., "Maintenance Activities of the American Redstart," *Wilson Bull.*, 74:153–65, 1962.
9. Hailman, J. P., "A Field Study of the Mocking Bird's Wing Flashing Behavior and Its Association with Foraging," *Wilson Bull.*, 72:346–57, 1960.
10. Hailman, J. P., "Insects Available for a Mocking Bird Wing Flashing in February," *Condor*, 62:405, 1960.
11. Johnston, R. F., and Hardy, J. W., "Behavior of the Purple Martin," *Wilson Bull.*, 74:243–62, 1962.
12. Kelso, L., and Nice, M. M., "A Russian Contribution to Anting and Feather Mites," *Wilson Bull.*, 75:23–26, 1963.
13. Melzack, R., *et al.*, "The Problem of Innate Fear of the Hawk Shape," *J. Comparative and Physiological Psychology*, 52:694–98, 1959.
14. Meyerriecks, A. J., "Foot Paddling Feeding Behavior in a Semipalmated Sandpiper," *Wilson Bull.*, 71:277, 1959.
15. Nice, M. M., *Development of Behavior in Precocial Birds* (New York: Linnaean Society, 1962).
16. Nice, M. M., "Head Scratching in Passerines," *Ibis*, 101:250–51, 1959.
17. Peterson, R. T., *The Bird* (New York: Time, Inc., 1963).
18. Roberts, B., "Notes on the Birds of Central and South-east Iceland with Special Reference to Food Habits," *Ibis*, 4:252, 1934.
19. Smith, S., and Hosking, E., *Birds Fighting* (London: Faber, 1955).
20. Thorpe, W. H., *Learning and Instinct in Animals* (Cambridge: Harvard University Press, 1956).

21. Tinbergen, N., *Bird Life* (London, Oxford University Press, 1954).
22. VanTyne, J., and Berger, A. J., *Fundamentals of Ornithology* (New York: John Wiley, 1959).
23. Welty, J. C., *The Life of Birds* (Philadelphia: Saunders, 1962).
24. Whitaker, L. M., "A Resumé of Anting with Particular Reference to a Captive Orchard Oriole," *Wilson Bull.*, 69:195–262, 1957.

CHAPTER V

1. Allen A. A., *The Book of Bird Life* (Princeton: Van Nostrand, 1961).
2. Anon., *Eastern Bird Banding Association News*, 26:34, 1963.
3. Austin, O. L., "Site Tenacity a Behavior Trait of the Common Tern," *Bird Banding*, 20:1–39, 1949.
4. Bellrose, F. C., "Celestial Orientation of Wild Mallards," *Bird Banding*, 29:75–90, 1958.
5. Bellrose, F. C., "Orientation Behavior of Four Species of Waterfowl," *Auk*, 80:257–89, 1963.
6. Borror, D. J., "A Check List of the Birds of Ohio," *Ohio J. of Science*, 50:1–32, 1950.
7. Brooks, W. S., "Effect of Weather on Autumn Shorebird Migration in East Central Illinois," *Wilson Bull.*, 77:45–54, 1965.
8. Cruickschank, A. D. and H. G., *One Thousand and One Questions Answered about Birds* (New York: Dodd, Mead, 1958).
9. Dorst, J., *The Migrations of Birds* (Boston: Houghton Mifflin, 1962).
10. Dorst, J., "Secrets of Migration," *Audubon Magazine*, 25:102–6, 1963.
11. Fromme, H. G., "Untersuchungen über das Orientierungs vermögen nachtlich ziehender Kleinvogel," *Ztsch. f. Tierpsychologie*, 18:205–20, 1961.
12. Graber, R. R., and Hassler, S. S., "The Effectiveness of Aircraft Type (APS) Radar in Detecting Birds," *Wilson Bull.* 74:367–80, 1962.
13. Hamilton, W. H., "Celestial Orientation in Juvenal Waterfowl," *Condor*, 64:19–33, 1962.
14. Hassler, S. S., *et. al.*, "Fall Migration and Weather: A Radar Study," *Wilson Bull*, 75:56–77, 1963.
15. Hoffman, K., "Experimental Manipulation of Orientational Clock in Birds," *Cold Springs Harbor Symposium On Quantitative Biology*, 25:379–87, 1960.

16. Howell, T. R., and Bartholomew, G. A., "Further Experiments on Torpidity in the Poor-will," *Condor*, 61:180–85, 1959.
17. Jaeger, E. C., "Further Observations on the Hibernation of the Poor-will," *Condor*, 51:105–9, 1949.
18. Kilham, L., "Breeding Behavior of Yellow-bellied Sapsuckers," *Auk*, 79:31–43, 1962.
19. Klemm, R., Public Lecture, Columbus, Ohio, Nov. 11, 1964.
20. Kramer, G., "Recent Experiments on Bird Orientation," *Ibis*, 101:399–416, 1959.
21. Lack, D., "Migration Across the Southern North Sea Studied by Radar," *Ibis*, 105:461–92, 1963.
22. Lasiewski, R. C., "The Energetics of Migrating Humming Birds," *Condor*, 64:324, 1962.
23. Lofts, B., *et al.*, "The Experimental Demonstration of Pre-migration Activity in the Absence of Fat Deposition in Birds," *Ibis*, 105:99–105, 1963.
24. Mahew, W. W., "Homing of Bank Swallows and Cliff Swallows," *Bird Banding*, 34:179–90, 1963.
25. Matthews, G. V. T., "Nonsense Orientation in Mallards and Its Relation to Experiments on Bird Navigation," *Ibis*, 103:211–30, 1961.
26. Matthews, G. V. T., "Sun Navigation in Homing Pigeons," *J. Exper. Biology*, 30:243–67, 1953.
27. Mewaldt, L. R., "California Sparrows Return from Displacement in Maryland," *Science*, 146:941–42, 1964.
28. Milne, L. J. and M., "Scientists Believe Animals Navigate by the Sun and Stars," *Audubon Magazine*, 64:26, 1962.
29. Miskimen, M., "Meteorological and Social Factors in Autumnal Migration of Ducks," *Condor*, 57:179–84, 1955.
30. Nisbet, I. C. T., "Measurements with Radar of the Height of Nocturnal Migrants over Cape Cod," *Bird Banding*, 34:57–67, 1963.
31. Raynor, G. S., "Meteorological Variables and the Northward Movement of Nocturnal Land Birds," *Auk*, 73:153–75, 1956.
32. Ruppel, W., "Zug der Jungen Störche ohne Führung der Alten," *Vogelzug*, 2:119–22, 1931.
33. Sauer, F., "Die Sternorientierung nächtlich ziehender Grasmücken," *Ztsch. f. Tierpsychologie*, 14:29–70, 1957.
34. Sauer, E. G., Star Navigation of Nocturnal Migrating Birds," *Cold Springs Harbor Symposium on Quantitative Biology*, 25:463–73, 1960.
35. Schmidt-Koenig, K., "Initial Orientation and Distance in the Pigeon," *Nature*, 201:638, 1964.

36. Schmidt-Koenig, K., "Internal Clocks and Homing," *Cold Springs Harbor Symposium on Quantitative Biology*, 25:389–93, 1960.
37. Stoddard, H. L., "Bird Casualties at a Leon County Florida TV Tower," *Tall Timbers Research Sta. Bull.*, 1:1–94, 1962.
38. Van Tyne, J., and Berger, A. J., *Fundamentals of Ornithology* (New York: John Wiley, 1959).
39. Vleugel, D. A., "Über die wahrscheinlichste Method der Wind-Orientierung ziehender Buchfinken," *Ornis Fennica*, 36:78–88, 1959.
40. Welty, J. C., *The Life of Birds* (Philadelphia: Saunders, 1962).

Chapter VI

1. Berger, A. J., *Bird Study* (New York: John Wiley, 1961).
2. Breland, K. and M., "Misbehavior of Organisms," *Amer. Psychologist*, 16:681–84, 1961.
3. Colias, N. E., "The Development of Social Behavior in Birds," *Auk*, 69:145, 1952.
4. Gottlieb, G., "Following Response Initiation in Ducklings: Age and Sensory Stimulation," *Science*, 140:399–400, 1963.
5. Gray, P. H., "Checklist of Papers Since 1951 Dealing with Imprinting in Birds," *Psychological Record*, 13:445–54, 1963.
6. Hess, E. H., "Two Conditions Limiting Age for Imprinting," *J. Comparative and Physiological Psychology*, 52: 515–18, 1959.
7. Hinde, R. A., "Factors Governing the Changes in Strength of a Partially Inborn Response as Shown by the Mobbing Behavior of the Chaffinch," *Proc. Royal Soc.*, 142:306–31, 1954.
8. Homberg, L., "Fiskande Kråkor," *Fauna och Flora*, 5:182–85, 1957.
9. James, H., and Binks, C., "Escape and Avoidance Learning in Newly Hatched Domestic Chicks," *Science*, 139:1293–94, 1963.
10. Jameson, W., *The Wandering Albatross* (Garden City: Doubleday, 1961).
11. Klopfer, P. H., "Social Interactions in Discrimination Learning with Special Reference to Feeding Behavior in Birds," *Behavior*, 14:282–99, 1959.
12. Klopfer, P. H., and Gottlieb, G., "Imprinting and Behavioral Polymorphism: Auditory and Visual Imprinting in Domestic Ducks and the Involvement of the Critical Period," *J. Comparative and Physiological Psychology*, 55:126–130, 1962.
13. Lack, D., *Darwin's Finches* (London: Cambridge University Press, 1947).

14. Lockley, R. M., *Puffins* (Garden City: Doubleday, 1962).
15. Lovell, H. B., "Baiting of Fish by Green Heron," *Wilson Bull.*, 70:280–81, 1958.
16. Rand, A. L., *Stray Feathers from a Bird Man's Desk* (Garden City: Doubleday, 1955).
17. Rice, C. E., "Imprinting by Force," *Science*, 138:680–81, 1962.
18. Sadovnikova, M. P., "A Study of the Behavior of Birds in the Maze," *J. Comparative and Physiological Psychology*, 3:123–39, 1923.
19. Smith, S., and Hosking, E., *Birds Fighting* (London: Faber, 1955).
20. Thompson, W. R., and O'Kiefe, M. W., "Imprinting: Its Effect on the Response to Stress in Chicks," *Science*, 135:918–19, 1962.
21. Tinbergen, N., *Bird Life* (London: Oxford University Press, 1954).
22. Vince, M. A., "String Pulling in Birds," *Behavior*, 17:103–29, 1961.

CHAPTER VII

1. Allen, A. A., *The Book of Bird Life* (Princeton: Van Nostrand, 1961).
2. Banks, R. C., "Birds Mobbing a Snake Skin," *Condor*, 59:213, 1957.
3. Baron, A., and Kish, G. B., "Early Social Isolation as a Determinant of Aggregative Behavior in the Domestic Chicken," *J. Comparative and Physiological Psychology*, 53:459–63, 1960.
4. Bartholomew, G. A., "The Fishing Activities of Double-crested Cormorants on San Francisco Bay," *Condor*, 44:13–21, 1942.
5. Beebe, F. L., "An Instance of Piracy by the Red-tailed Hawk on the Peregrine Falcon," *Condor*, 62:480–81, 1960.
6. Berger, A. J., "The Cowbird and Certain Host Species in Michigan," *Wilson Bull.*, 63:26–34, 1951.
7. Brewer, R. C., "Comparative Notes on the Life History of the Carolina Chickadee," *Wilson Bull.*, 73:348–73, 1961.
8. Colias, N. E., "Some Mechanisms of Family Integration in Ducks," *Auk*, 73:378–400, 1956.
9. Davis, D. E., "The Phylogeny of Social Nesting Habits in the *Crotophaginae*," *Quart. Rev. of Biology*, 17:115–34, 1942.
10. Ficken, M. S., "Redstarts and Cowbirds," *Kingbird*, pp. 2, July, 1961.

11. Ficken, R. W., "Courtship and Agonistic Behavior of the Common Grackle," *Auk*, 80:52–72, 1963.
12. Gobeil, R. E., "The Comparative Feeding Behavior of Wintering Evening Grosbeaks and Purple Finches," *Bird Banding*, 34:217–18, 1963.
13. Hailman, J. P., "Unusual Bunching Behavior of Starlings," *Condor*, 61:369, 1959.
14. Hall, H. M., *A Gathering of Shore Birds* (New York: Devin-Adair, 1961).
15. Hamilton, W. J., "Aggressive Behavior in Migrant Pectoral Sandpipers," *Condor*, 61:161–79, 1959.
16. Hergenrode, G. L., "The Incidence of Nest Parasitism by the Brown Headed Cowbird on Roadside Nesting Birds in Nebraska," *Auk*, 79:85–88, 1962.
17. Jenkins, D., "Social Behavior in the Partridge," *Ibis*, 103a:155, 1961.
18. Mayfield, H., "The Kirtland's Warbler," *Cranbrook Inst. of Sci. Bull.*, No. 40, 242 pp. 1960.
19. Muhl, K., "Die Star als Winterlicher Nutzniesser von Schafherden," *Die Vogelwarte*, 19:36–38, 1957.
20. Putnam, W. L., "Starling Feeds Nestling Robins," *Canadian Field Naturalist*, 75:52–53, 1961.
21. Rand, A. L., *Stray Feathers from a Bird Man's Desk* (Garden City: Doubleday, 1955).
22. Rice, D. W., "Associations with Elephants and Hippopotamuses," *Auk*, 80:196–97, 1963.
23. Selander, R. K., and LaRue, C. J., "Interspecific Preening Invitation Display of Parasitic Cowbirds," *Auk*, 78:473–504, 1961.
24. Skutch A. F., "Helpers Among Birds," *Condor*, 63:198–206, 1961.
25. Skutch, A. F., "The Nest as a Dormitory," *Ibis*, 103a:50–70, 1961.
26. Skutch, A. F., "Roosting and Nesting of Aracari Toucans," *Condor*, 60:201–19, 1958.
27. Sparks, J. H., "Significance of Allopreening in the Red Avadavat and Its Development in Other Birds," *Nature*, 200:281, 1963.
28. Verrill, A. H., *Strange Birds and Their Stories* (New York: Page, 1938).
29. Weller, M. W., "Parasitic Egg Laying in the Redhead and Other North American *Anatidae*," *Ecology Monog.* 29:333–65, 1959.
30. Young, H., "Breeding Success of the Cowbird," *Wilson Bull.*, 75:115–22, 1963.

CHAPTER VIII

1. Allen, A. A., *The Book of Bird Life* (Princeton: Van Nostrand, 1961).
2. Armstrong, E. A., A *Study of Bird Song* (London: Oxford University Press, 1963).
3. Baird, J., "Hostile Displays of Rose-breasted Grosbeaks Toward a Red Squirrel," *Wilson Bull.*, 76:286–89, 1964.
4. Berger, A. J., *Bird Study* (New York: John Wiley, 1961).
5. Borror, D. J., "Bird Song," *Audubon Magazine*, 67:159–63, 1965.
6. Cullen, E., "Adaptations in the Kittiwake to Cliff Nesting," *Ibis*, 99:275–302, 1957.
7. Ficken, M. S. and R. W., "The Comparative Ethology of Wood Warblers," *The Living Bird*, 1:103–22, 1962.
8. Frings, H., "The Language of Crows," *Sci. Amer.*, 20:119 ff., 1951.
9. Frings, H. and M., "Bio-Acoustics and Pest Control," *Bio-Acoustics Bull.*, 2:21–24, 1962.
10. Haartman, L. V., "Territory in the Pied Flycatcher," *Ibis*, 98:460–75, 1956.
11. Kilham, L., "Behavior and Methods of Communication of Pileated Woodpeckers," *Condor*, 61:377–87, 1959.
12. Lanyon, W. E., *The Ontogeny of Vocalizations in Birds*, A.I.B.S. Publ. No. 7 (Washington, 1960), 321–47.
13. Laskey, A. R., "A Study of the Cardinal in Tennessee," *Wilson Bull.*, 56:27–44, 1944.
14. Leopold, A., and Eynor, A. E., "Avian Daybreak and Evening Song in Relation to Time and Light Intensities," *Condor*, 63:269–93, 1961.
15. Marler, P., *Bird Songs and Mate Selection*, A.I.B.S. (Washington, 1960), 348–67.
16. Marler, P., and Tamura, M., "Culturally Transmitted Patterns of Vocal Behavior in Sparrows," *Science*, 146:1483–86, 1964.
17. Marler, P., *et al.* "Song Development in Hand Reared Oregon Juncoes," *Auk*, 79:12–30, 1962.
18. Penney, R. L., *The Adélie Penguin's Faithfulness to Territory and Mate* (Paris: Biologie Antarctique, 1964), 401–6.
19. Peterson, R. T., *The Bird* (New York, Time, Inc., 1963).
20. Saunders, A. A., "The Song of the Song Sparrow," *Wilson Bull.* 63:99–109, 1951.
21. Selander, R. K., and Giller, D. R., "Analysis of Sympatry of Great-tailed and Boat-tailed Grackles," *Condor*, 63:29–86, 1961.

22. Selander, R. K., and LaRue, C. J., "Interspecific Preening Invitation Display of Parasitic Cowbirds," *Auk*, 78:473–504, 1961.
23. Stokes, A. W., "Voice and Social Behavior of the Chukar Partridge," *Condor*, 63:111–27, 1961.
24. Thorpe, W. H., "The Learning of Song Patterns by Birds with Especial Reference to the Song of the Chaffinch," *Ibis*, 100:535–70, 1958.
25. Tinbergen, N., *Bird Life* (London: Oxford University Press, 1954).

Chapter IX

1. Allen, A. A., *The Book of Bird Life* (Princeton: Van Nostrand, 1961).
2. Anderson, A. H., "Life History of the Cactus Wren," *Condor*, 62:351–69, 1960.
3. Baerends, G. P., "The Ethological Analysis of Incubation Behavior," *Ibis*, 101:357–68, 1959.
4. Brewer, R., "Comparative Notes on the Life History of the Carolina Chickadee," *Wilson Bull.*, 73:348–73, 1961.
5. Colias, N. E., "The Development of Social Behavior in Birds," *Auk*, 69:127–59, 1952.
6. Drury, W. H., "Studies of the Breeding Biology of Horned Lark, Water Pipit, Lapland Longspur and Snow Bunting," *Bird Banding*, 32:1–46, 1961.
7. Ficken, M. S., "Nest-Site Selection in the American Redstart," *Wilson Bull.*, 76:189–90, 1964.
8. Ficken, R. W., "Courtship and Agonistic Behavior in the Common Grackle, *Auk*, 80:52–72, 1963.
9. Gilliard, J. W., "The Evolution of Bower Birds," *Sci. Amer.*, 209:38–46, 1963.
10. Goertz, J. W., "An Opossum-Titmouse Incident," *Wilson Bull.*, 74:189–90, 1962.
11. Gottlieb, G., "A Naturalistic Study of Imprinting in Wood Ducklings," *J. Comparative Physiological Psychology*, 56:86–91, 1963.
12. Hoyt, S. F., "Nest Building Movements Performed by Juvenal Song Sparrow," *Wilson Bull.*, 73:386, 1961.
13. Kilham, L., "Courtship and Territorial Behavior in Hairy Woodpeckers," *Auk*, 77:259–70, 1960.
14. Levi, W. M., *The Pigeon* (Columbia, S.C.: Bryan Co., N.D.) p. 512.

15. Nice, M. M., *The Watcher at the Nest* (New York: Macmillan, 1939).
16. Nolan, V., "Blue-jay Sitting on Robin Nest in December," *Condor*, 60:405–6, 1958.
17. Parks, G. H. and H. C., "Some Notes on a Trip to an Evening Grosbeak Nesting Area," *Bird Banding*, 34:22–30, 1963.
18. Rice, D. W., and Kenyon, K. W., "Breeding Cycles and Behavior of Laysan and Blackfooted Albatrosses," *Auk*, 79:517–67, 1962.
19. Stewart, P. A., "Nesting Attentiveness and Incubation Period of Wood Duck," *Bird Banding*, 33:85–89, 1962.
20. Verrill, A. H., *Strange Birds and Their Stories* (New York: Page, 1938).
21. Watson, G. E., "A Simultaneous Nesting of the Robin and Blue Jay," *Auk*, 80:377, 1963.

Chapter X

1. Allen, A. A., *The Book of Bird Life* (Princeton: Van Nostrand, 1961).
2. Brooks-King, M., and Harrell, H. G., "Intelligence Tests with Birds," *British Birds*, 51:514–24, 1958.
3. Colias, N. S., and Taber, R. D., "A Field Study of Some Grouping and Dominance Relations in Ring-necked Pheasants," *Condor*, 53:265–75, 1951.
4. Ferguson-Lee, I. J., "Studies of Aggressive *Capercaillie*," *British Birds*, 56:19–22, 1963.
5. Fisher, J., and Hinde, R. A., "The Opening of Milk Bottles by Birds," *British Birds*, 42:347–57, 1949.
6. Guhl, A. M., "The Development of Social Organization in the Domestic Chick," *J. Animal Behavior*, 6:92–111, 1958.
7. Hanson, H. S., "Inter-Family Dominance in Canada Geese," *Auk*, 70:11–16, 1953.
8. Lack, D., *The Life of the Robin* (London: Witherby, 1946).
9. Laskey, A. R., "Breeding Biology of Mockingbirds," *Auk*, 79:596–606, 1962.
10. Marks, H. L., *et al.*, "Effect of Comb and Wattle Removal on the Social Organization of Mixed Flocks of Chickens," *Animal Behavior*, 8:192–96, 1960.
11. Matthewson, S. F., "Gonadotrophic Hormones Affect Aggressive Behavior in Starlings," *Science*, 134:1522–23, 1961.
12. Murphy, J. R., "Aggressive Behavior of the Bald Eagle," *Auk*, 79:712, 1962.

13. Murphy, R. C., *Oceanic Birds of South America* (New York: Macmillan, 1936).
14. Nice, M. M., "Development of Behavior in Precocial Birds," *Transactions of Linnaean Society*, Vol. 8, 1962.
15. Nice, M. M., "Studies in the Life History of the Song Sparrow," *Transactions of Linnaean Society*, Vol. 2, 6:1–328, 1943.
16. Norris, R. A., "Relative Incidence of Distress Calls or Squeals in Mist Netted Birds," *Bird Banding*, 36:83–88, 1965.
17. Parks, G. H., "Male Junco 'Weds' His Own Daughter," *Bird Banding*, 19:22, 1948.
18. Pennychick, C. J., and Webbe, D., "Observations on Fulmars in Spitzbergen," *British Birds*, 52:321–332, 1959.
19. Peterson, R. T., *The Bird* (New York, Time, Inc., 1963).
20. Ratner, S. C., "Effects of Learning to Be Submissive on Status in the Peck Order of Domestic Fowl," *Animal Behavior*, 9:34–37, 1961.
21. Sabine, W. S., "Winter Society of Oregon Junco," *Condor*, 61:110–135, 1959.
22. Serventy, D. L., *et al.*, "Trapping and Maintaining Shore Birds in Captivity," *Bird Banding*, 33:123–130, 1962.
23. Skutch, A. F., "The Parental Devotion of Birds," *Sci. Monthly*, 62:364–74, 1964.
24. Smith, S., and Hosking, E., *Birds Fighting* (London: Faber, 1955).
25. Smith, V., and Hale, E. B., "Modification of Social Rank in Domestic Fowl," *J. Comparative and Physiological Psychology*, 52:373–75, 1959.
26. Tinbergen, N., "Comparative Studies of the Behavior of Gulls," *Behavior*, 15:1–70, 1960.
27. Verrill, A. H., *Strange Birds and Their Stories* (New York: Page, 1938).
28. Welty, J. C., *The Life of Birds* (Philadelphia: Saunders, 1962).

INDEX

INDEX